C000178436

Wild Flowers
of **Mann**

Written by Andree Dubbeldam
on behalf of Wildflowers of Mann
Edited by Trevor Barrett

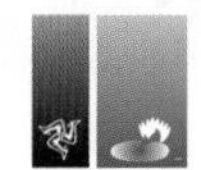

First published in 2004 by Lily Publications Ltd
PO Box 33 Ramsey, Isle of Man IM99 4LP
Telephone: 01624 898446 Fax: 01624 898449 ISBN: 1 899602 3 72

CONTENTS

ACKNOWLEDGEMENTS

The creation of this book has been made possible with the help of many people, but special thanks go to the Wildflowers of Mann Project committee members: Bill Henderson (MHK), Martin Quayle (MHK), Dominic Delaney (MLC), Colvyn Quaggin (Department of Transport), Geoff Le Page (Department of Tourism and Leisure), Kevin Griffiths (Department of Tourism and Leisure), Liz Charter (Department of Agriculture, Fisheries and Forestry), Kate Hawkins (Manx National Heritage), Duncan Bridges (Manx Wildlife Trust), Alice Quayle (Isle of Man Friends of the Earth), Ian Sleight (Manx Farmers Union), Harvey Briggs (Isle of Man Newspapers), Ian Quayle (Farming and Wildlife Advisory Group).

Advice, pictures and other help have been received from John Callister, Ian Costain, Miles Cowsill, Larch Garrad, Mike Goldie, Andrew Lowe, Maura Mitchell, Linda Moore, Cilla Platt, Clare Price, Barbara Speirs, Aline Thomas and Philippa Tomlinson. Special thanks also go to Deb Andrews.

Thanks to Isle of Man Friends of the Earth for additional funding.

Foreword

Manx by name and Manx by nature

The Isle of Man is of course thrice blessed. It is an island set in a sea that feels the benefit of what we used to call the Gulf Stream. It has elevation, Snaefell rising to 2,037 feet above the waves, and it now has this fascinating little book that recounts its natural history in the true 'common sense' of the word.

Life on any island depends on traditional knowledge of available resources, a fact that is in essence as true for plants as for people. So as Manxmen and women discovered their virtues, names were named and heritage did the rest. A few must suffice to whet your imagination.

The quicksilver leaves of Aspen gave it the name Chengey Mraaee, Woman's Tongue. Jeimyn Yee, the Fuchsia Flower that drips from stunted hedgerows that braid the sod hedges, just had to be God's Tears. The Red Campion Blaa ny Ferrishin means Fairy Flower and Fairy Doctors plied their trade in herbal medicines until recent times.

The Giant Puffball probably got its name Cabbyl Mooyn, meaning horse pee, from the russet stream that ejaculates from its monstrous fungus when shedding what is said to be the world record number of spores.

A favourite plant of mine is the Isle of Man Cabbage. Though not the most outstanding, it is certainly well worth seeing for it was first described from the Island and is a special part of genetic diversity that has counselled children to eat up their greens since time immemorial.

A favourite place is much easier, and my choice goes to the Ayres, that diverse tract of land at the northern tip of the Island. Tough yet vulnerable, its lichen heath, well grazed by rabbits, bursts with special biodiversity. Sand spiced with seashells constantly blows ashore, adding lime to the mix, a fact rewarded by hosts of Pyramidal Orchids that flower in due season, and swathes of Birdsfoot Trefoil, whose nectar-rich flowers feed myriad insects and perpetuate the song of the skylark..

Sadly much has gone, starting with the forest that once covered most of the land, replaced long ago by the necessity of grazing and cropland, and still threatened by inappropriate development like sculptured landfill. All part of the rich tapestry of Island life.

But help is at hand - a partnership of caring people led by Manx Wildlife Trust. Appropriate legislation is now in place, as are reserves and a National Nature Reserve. Two visitor centres educate locals and tourists alike, while the Wildflowers of Mann Project is beginning to stitch the Island back together with truly native stock.

This lovely Island has more than its fair share of exotic plants that have made their home here, but perversely a much more insidious threat is the introduction of alien stock of these native Manx plants. Even the most common native flowers are somewhat different from those of the adjacent land masses. They may share the same Latin names but they are Manx by nature, showing evolution is still underway. This visionary programme is starting to spread the local gene stock back across the Island.

David Bellamy

Bedburn - May 2004

Isle of Man Government

Manx Telecom Ltd
Isle of Man Business Park, Cooil Road
Braddan, Isle of Man
IM99 1HX
Telephone: +44 (0)1624 633633 (general enquiries) Fax: +44 (0)1624 636011

Bradford & Bingley
International

Bradford & Bingley International
30 Ridgeway Street
Douglas, Isle of Man, IM1 1TA
Telephone: +44 (0) 1624 695000 Fax: +44 (0) 1624 695001
Email: enquiries@bbi.co.im Website: www.bbi.co.im

Total Isle of Man Ltd
Mill Road
Peel, Isle of Man, IM5 1TB
Telephone: +44 (0) 1624 844000 Fax: +44 (0) 1624 842969
Website: www.total.co.im

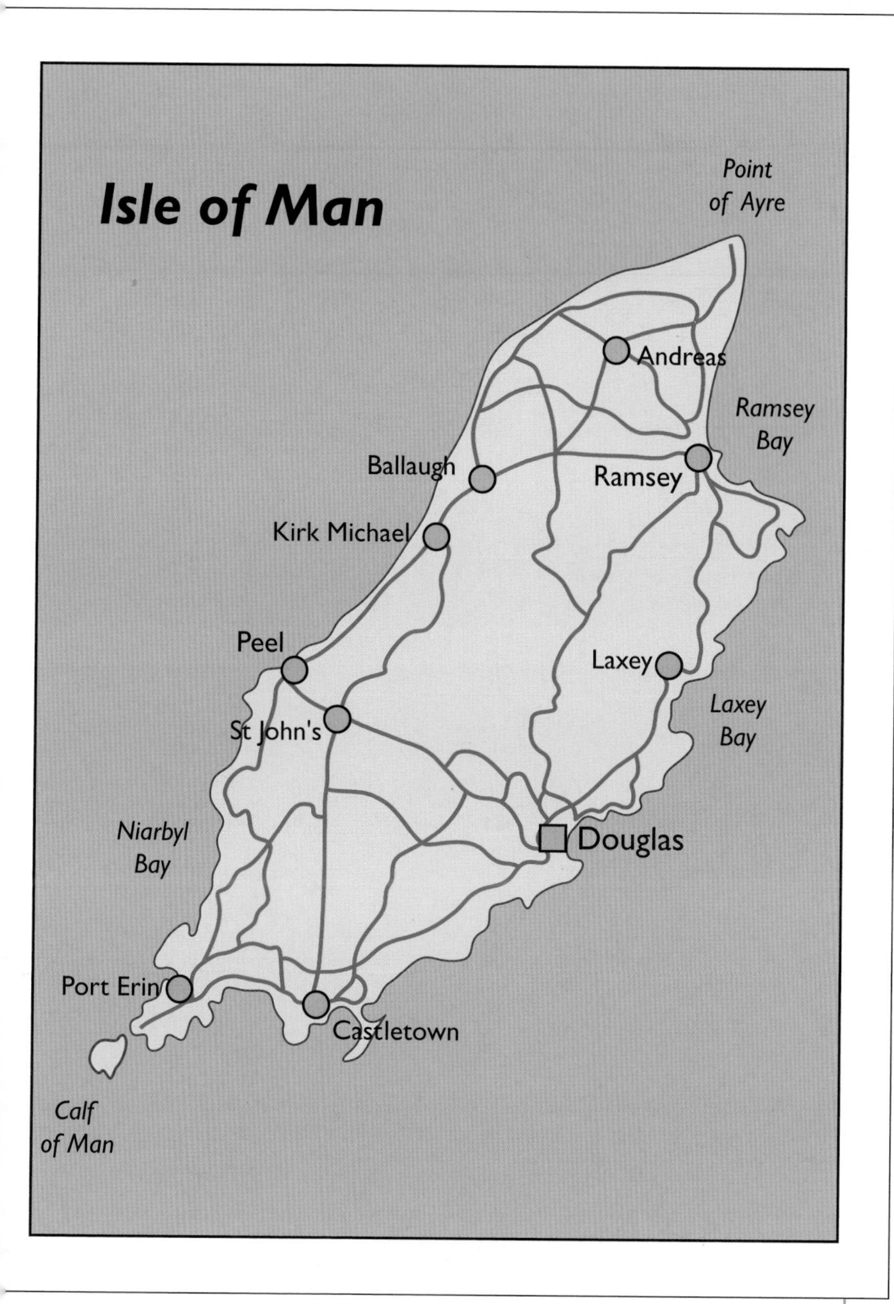
Isle of Man
Point of Ayre
Andreas
Ramsey Bay
Ballaugh
Ramsey
Kirk Michael
Peel
Laxey
Laxey Bay
St John's
Niarbyl Bay
Douglas
Port Erin
Castletown
Calf of Man

Harebell. *(Vicki Harrop)*

Common Spotted Orchid. *(Vicki Harrop)*

The origins of the Island's wild flowers

Go back 15,000 years and the world was in the grip of the last ice age. The land mass which was to become the Isle of Man was a frozen waste. Yet the flora so familiar on the Island today was actually growing then – but far away, around the area which we now know as Spain.

Move forward in time by about 3,500 years and the earth was warming up. The ice was retreating and plants were colonising. There was still no Isle of Man yet: sea levels were much lower than they are today and there was no Irish Sea, North Sea or English Channel. So plants and animals in the south which had survived the glacial period were able to spread north unimpeded over the bare soils and rocks left behind by the ice.

Hazel flower. Though commonly planted, the hazel tree is restricted to a few mountain and coastal sites as a wild plant. ***(Ian Costain)***

Arctic plants such as tough grasses and low-growing wild flowers, mosses and lichen would have been the first to colonise, soon to be replaced by birch and then pine forests so typical of the Highlands of Scotland today.

As the climate became warmer, trees such as oak and elm and shrubs such as hazel would have dominated (and would still dominate today were it not for the eventual arrival of human settlers) and many of the flowers we now consider common on the Island would have been restricted

Ox-eye daisy. One of several wild flowers classed as 'possibly native'. Determining if a plant is native or not is largely down to the judgement of ecologists. *(Ian Costain)*

to the most exposed coastal zones and natural forest glades.

The rising temperature and the meltwater from the retreating ice sheets created a corresponding rise in sea levels. Consequently, around 10,000 years ago the last land bridge between the Isle of Man and the rest of the British Isles was closed. Before the Island was cut off a significant number of plants would have colonised, but some, if not most, arrived subsequently by various natural means – wind, birds and sea.

Many of these first (native) wild plants have become extinct over time. Today about 700 flowering plants – including trees and grasses – and as many species of moss and lichen are considered to be native to the Isle of Man. Approximately three times this number of species are native to the rest of the British Isles.

Native plant populations have virtually been isolated from their British cousins since the Island was formed. This has allowed them to evolve and adapt perfectly to local conditions. Even though eight to ten thousand years is quite a short time in evolutionary terms, and the changes are very subtle, the Island's native populations are nonetheless unique.

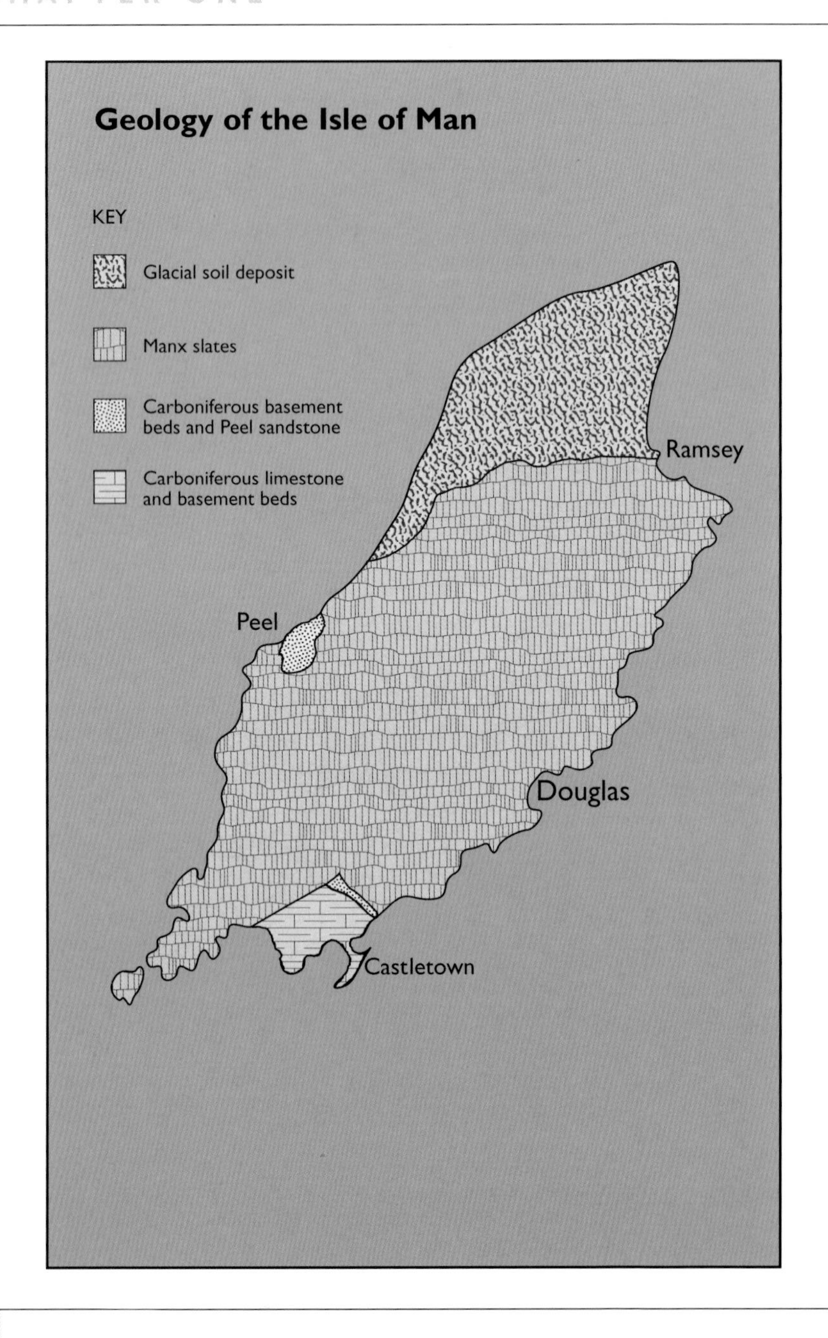
Geology of the Isle of Man
KEY
Glacial soil deposit
Manx slates
Carboniferous basement beds and Peel sandstone
Carboniferous limestone and basement beds
Ramsey
Peel
Douglas
Castletown

Least Willow - *Salix herbacea*

Calling this little shrub 'least' willow is something of an understatement, as it grows to just a few millimetres high, making it the Island's smallest shrub. A cold-loving plant, it is found only on the top of Snaefell, where it can tolerate the harshest mountain conditions. Like all willows, its flowers are yellow catkins which appear as late as May/June.

What makes this wild flower remarkable is that it is one of the oldest surviving species on the Island – the only relic of the arctic/alpine flora that first colonised here after the last ice age. Evidence of this early existence has been found preserved in peat thousands of years old on the northern plain, alongside the remains of Irish elk – giant deer which roamed the Isle of Man when it had a sub-arctic climate.

Least willow is now very rare on the Island and global warming poses a real threat to its future survival here.

THE FORMATION OF A MANX DUB

As a glacier retreats it sometimes leaves behind huge blocks of ice.

As the ice melts it leaves behind a depression called a kettle hole.

The kettle hole may silt up with marl, a white clay, and peat may form around the surface.

The fertile marl was often dug out to improve surrounding land.

The kettle hole becomes a pond or 'dub' and rapidly begins to silt up again.

(Alice Quayle)

Least willow. *(Linda Moore)*

Field Scabious - *Knautia arvensis*

The pastel mauve of the field scabious is a familiar sight in the south-east of the Island, where it flowers in late summer. Elsewhere it is rather uncommon, thriving only on alkaline soils such as those over the limestone around Castletown. A sun-loving wild flower, it can be found in verges and meadows, but as its range coincides with some of the most fertile farmland, it has been pushed out of many of its former habitats by intensive farming practices.

Field Scabious. *(Linda Moore)*

Bog myrtle. A plant with many traditional uses, from flavouring beer to keeping midges away.
(Manx National Heritage)

The little pincushion flowers are a favourite of butterflies, bees and flower arrangers, the latter able to grow this plant in back gardens for cut flowers.

A home for wild flowers

For a small island, the Isle of Man has surprisingly varied soils, climate and geology – variations which dictate where all the wild flowers would naturally occur, as each species is adapted to its own range of conditions (its niche).

The rocks of the Island date back millions of years and originated in very different conditions from those prevailing today. Limestone was formed in shallow tropical seas, where the shells of tiny marine creatures fell to the sea bed as an ooze and slowly developed into a thick layer of stone. Over millions of years this has been compressed into the tough limestones around Castletown. Sandstone, found around Peel, is made of compressed sand originating in a semi-desert landscape. The oldest rocks – up to 490 million years old – are the slate (or Manx Group Rocks) of the Island's mountain areas and most originated at

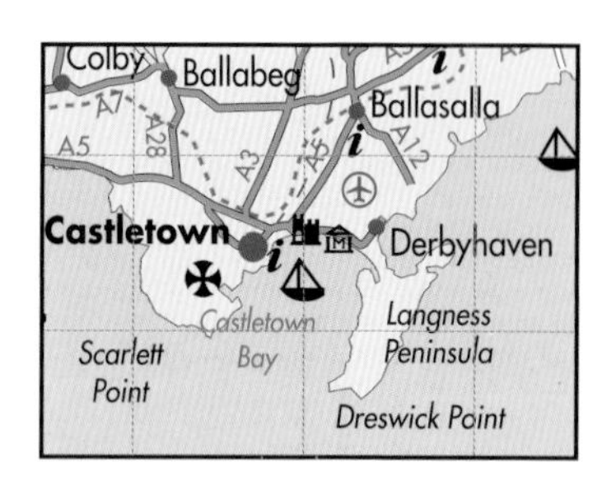

the edge of an ancient ocean from deposits of silt, sand and clay.

410 million years ago, the rocks of the Manx Group were folded, crumpled and cracked by a period of movement in the earth's crust. Heat and pressure generated by this upheaval changed the rocks chemically, and led to the deposition of the metal ores which were the foundation of the Island's mining industry in the 1700 and 1800s. Eventually these ancient rocks were exposed by uplift in the crust and erosion of the younger sediments above them.

Soils determine where many wild flowers can survive. Thus lime lovers such as field scabious favour the soils around Castletown, while wild carrot (*Daucus carota*) is at its most common on the free-draining sands around Peel.

Many soils do not originate from the bedrock at all but are more recent sediments deposited by retreating ice (as on the northern plain) or are peaty soils made up of thousands of years of partly-decayed plant remains (as found in the Ballaugh Curragh and mountain peat bogs). These peaty soils support many specialised plants such as bog myrtle (*Myrica gale*), cotton grass (*Eriophorum angustifolium)* and sundew (*Drosera rotundifolia*).

The Manx climate and topography also dictate where plants can grow. For instance, the sea wind would scorch many inland wild flowers, but the dozens of

Scarlett in flower. *(Linda Moore)*

Scarlett limestone showing the layers, each representing hundreds of thousands of years of sediments.

species found along the coast, such as thrift and sea campion, are perfectly adapted to such conditions.

Tough heathers can tolerate harsh winds and cool summers, so adapt well to mountain conditions. Sheltered valley bottoms with nutrient-rich water washed down from the hills are the favoured habitat for wetland plants such as marsh marigold (*Caltha palustris*) and meadowsweet (*Filipendula ulmaria*).

Woodlands are home to some of the Island's most loved wild flowers which are especially adapted to making use of early spring sunlight before the tree canopy comes into leaf. The Island is particularly noted for its displays of bluebells (*Hyacinthoides non-scriptus*) and wild garlic (*Allium ursinum*).

Scarlett

Scarlett Point is a popular beauty spot in the Island's south, renowned for the geological features exposed here by the sea. The Scarlett story goes back over 300 million years. Then it was a shallow tropical sea at the equator with calcium sediments accumulating from the remains of dead sea life. A period of intense volcanic activity, in which huge amounts of volcanic rock were born (often in just hours), brought to an end 60 million years of limestone formation.

These volcanic rocks, limestone and fossils are what makes Scarlett special today, but the rocks are also overlain with grassland as rich in wild flower species as you can find anywhere on the Island. At any time between May and October there will be something in flower, but in May and June the carpets of flowers are so dense it is impossible to put a foot down without stepping on them.

In summertime, cotton grass transforms mountain bogs.

Stars of this show are thrift (*Armeria maritima*), bird's-foot trefoil (*Lotus corniculatus*) and sea campion (*Silene uniflora*), but closer inspection will reveal a bewildering number of different species including purple milk vetch (*Astragalus danicus*), a plant rare elsewhere in the British Isles.

As well as the grassland, small brackish pools are dotted around and contain a mix of species that, while not conspicuous, are attractive when looked at close up. Good examples are sea milkwort (*Glaux maritima*) and sea arrowgrass (*Triglochin palustris*). Towards Castletown Bay the sheltered shingle storm beach has the deadly 8-foot-high hemlock (*Conium maculatum*), tree mallow (*Lavatera arborea*) and drifts of long-headed poppy (*Papaver dubium*).

Cotton Grass - *Eriophorum angustifolium*

To the untrained eye one sedge looks much the same as any other, but cotton grass is the exception. On the extensive open bogs where it is found, this plant often occurs in large drifts, its fluffy white seed heads marking out areas of waterlogged ground. In winter the leaves turn a copper colour and look metallic in the winter sun.

Common daisy has found human habitats such as lawns much to its liking. *(Barbara Spiers)*

Cotton grass tends to be found with other plants of acid bog such as sundew, bog asphodel (*Narthecium ossifragum*) and deer grass. But beware – wherever you see these plants growing together you'll probably find deep bogs, ideal for losing your wellies!

Cotton grass is common on many of the upland parts of the Island as well as a few lowland sites such as the Ballaugh Curragh and the Ayres.

Meadowsweet - *Filipendula ulmaria*

From ditch bottoms and damp meadows to pond sides and curragh, this wild flower will grow almost anywhere that is wet. It can grow in full sun or woodland and can spread by suckering roots or seed. Needless to say, it is still a very common Manx wild flower.

In July and August meadowsweet is adorned with frothy sweet-smelling flower heads. Strangely, this is not the origin of its English name, which comes from its use as a flavouring of mead (an alcoholic drink made from honey). The plant also contains a natural painkiller and was used as a medicinal herb.

Forests and fields beneath the waves

Manx flora does not end where the land ends. When you reach the sea there begins a mysterious and fascinating world of algae known as seaweeds. Over 300 species are known to occur around the Island. Along the beach you can find the wracks such as bladder wrack that can survive periodic dry spells as the tide goes in and out. These plants shelter a range of crabs, shrimps and molluscs much prized (and prised!) by the wading birds that forage along the tide line.

Unseen by people this kelp forest grows just 100 metres from St Michaels Isle. *(Maura Mitchell)*

Offshore kelp forests occur frequently because of the Isle of Man's clear waters and strong nutrient-rich currents. These sheltering forests provide ideal hiding places for young sea creatures and are the ocean's nursery. The bounty of creatures inhabiting the kelp also sustains the Island's native seal population, as well as providing feeding grounds for porpoises and dolphins.

Only one flowering plant survives permanently beneath the sea. The eelgrass (*Zostera marina*) is found in shallow water where it can form 'meadows', but it is quite rare around the Island.

The first peoples and last forests

Stone Age human colonisation of the Isle of Man came soon after the wild flowers. For thousands of years the effect on the landscape would have been minimal, the hunter gatherer communities relying on the natural environment

Meadowsweet

(especially the coast) to sustain them.

The advent of farming in the late Stone Age (about 3,000 BC) began the transformation of the Island from forest to open farms. Excavations of the 'Ronaldsway' peoples (named after the site where evidence of them was found) have revealed that the crops they grew had weeds from southern Europe and that they used stone tools originating from Ireland and the Lake District. This basic early 'technology' meant that for a thousand years farms were limited to clearings within the forest. The clearings were often temporary and restricted to easily-worked soils.

The end of the extensive Manx forests came in the Bronze Age, when large herds of domesticated animals grazed the mountains and the metal ploughs tilled the valley soils. It is likely that by the Iron Age (the Celtic era), the only woodlands left were those needed for charcoal (for smelting metal ores) and for building materials. The remaining woods were progressively destroyed over the years, and records show that by the 16th century the Island was largely devoid of trees and woodlands.

The loss of woodland cover led to the extinction of many species of plant and animal, the latter including deer and wild cats and numerous others. But for wild flowers it was a happier story: in the place of forests came new habitats such as hay meadows for orchids, cornfields for poppies and heathland for heathers.

Bird's-foot trefoil flower. *(Barbara Spiers)*

Bird's-Foot Trefoil - *Lotus corniculatus*

This is a plant with dozens of local names, such as bacon and eggs and lady's fingers. Bird's-foot trefoil can be found in any sunny, dry, short turf, so is equally at home on Manx sod hedges, sea cliffs and old lawns. In late spring bees are attracted to the golden yellow flowers, which are that bit brighter than the surrounding buttercups and dandelions.

One of this wild flower's main virtues is its role as the food plant of the caterpillar of the common blue butterfly (*Polyommatus icarus*) – one of the Island's prettiest insects. In wetter soils the common bird's-foot trefoil (*Lotus comiculatus*) is replaced by the greater bird's-foot trefoil (*Lotus pedunculatus*)– a larger and later-flowering relative.

The modern landscape

Today the Manx landscape is divided between open upland and enclosed lowlands. The hills are largely heather moorland, but where grazing is heavier this is replaced by grass. Some parts of the uplands have been converted to conifer plantations in the past 60 years. The lowlands are a more intimate mix of

Arrivals such as poppies were introduced by the first farmers thousands of years ago. *(Vicki Harrop)*

farmsteads, byways, hay meadows, pasture, sod hedges and intensively farmed areas.

In the late 19th century many of the Island's narrow valleys were planted with trees and became ornamental pleasure gardens. Now, more than 100 years on, they are virtually the only mature broadleaf woodland on the Island. Many have been bought by the Isle of Man Government and are protected and managed as Manx national glens.

Over time, as pressure for development on the Island has increased, parts of the landscape have undergone dramatic change. Initially, although such change can be very damaging, in the longer term it can provide a home for wild flowers. Examples include reservoirs, which develop a fringe of wetland, and new housing estates, which when mature have an abundance of trees and shrubs (well patronised by nesting birds) and gardens in which wild flowers are either planted or creep in uninvited, such as daisies do in lawns.

With increasing awareness of the need to protect wildlife and the environment, conservationists and planning authorities are now helping to steer development away from the most sensitive areas in which Manx wild flowers thrive. At the same time, schemes to incorporate native wild flowers into new developments wherever possible are also being actively encouraged.

In summer, common blue butterflies can be seen along cliff tops where bird's-foot trefoil grows in abundance. ***(Barbara Spiers)***

History, folklore and flora

The folklore surrounding wild flowers is as rich on the Isle of Man as it is anywhere in western Europe, and some customs and tales still survive.

The Island's folklore has its roots in pagan Celtic and Viking belief as much as in medieval European Christian traditions. Some lore is a fusion of many traditions, a Christian veneer applied to pagan beliefs to make them palatable to the clergy. Given very little written documentary evidence, it is often hard to differentiate between real 'Manx' traditions and those made up or imported from Ireland in the Celtic revival of the 19th and early 20th centuries.

Wild flowers would have been much more familiar to people in the past, as they were an intrinsic part of everyday life and culture. Wild flowers were used for food, textiles, dyes and medicines. They were symbolic in festivals and religion. They were used to flavour drink and to make household poisons, and in times of famine they were all that stood between a population and death.

Manx Gaelic names for wild flowers largely died out with the language but some, such as bollan bane for mugwort (*Artemisia vulgaris*) and cushag for ragwort (*Senecio jacobaea*), are still in common use on the Island. Other Manx names have survived in a translated form, an example being red campion (*Silene dioica*), which is still called fairy flower – a direct translation from blaa ny ferrishin.

Many of the traditions relating to wild flowers were based on a superstitious interpretation of their properties. Hence the sticky-leafed sundew could be covertly placed upon a person to ensnare that person in love, and a plant with

European gorse. *(Vicki Harrop)*

yellow sap could be a cure for jaundice.

Many traditional cures are now recognised in modern medicine. The foxglove (*Digitalis purpurea*), long employed as a means to steady the heart, is now the basis of a conventional laboratory-made heart medicine, and comfrey (*Symphytum spp.*) is used to help heal wounds and bruises.

Much of Manx plant folklore revolves around protection from supernatural phenomena such as fairies and witches, who bore the blame for the suffering and inexplicable events encountered in people's lives.

Cushag

The Manx national plant, cushag (or ragwort as it is known in the rest of the British Isles) has as many critics as it has admirers. The golden flowers are

God's Tears – the poetic Manx name for the fuschsia flower.

undoubtedly pretty and manage to grow on roadsides, lawns, beaches, sea cliffs and pastureland. The plant is welcomed by conservationists as it is host to dozens of insect species and a favourite nectar plant for moths, bees and butterflies. But to farmers, cushag is a deadly poisonous plant, responsible for many livestock fatalities. Animals avoid it when the plant is green and carries a warning in its bitter taste, but when cushag is cut and dry no such warning is apparent and livestock will eat it.

The colour of the flower is also alluded to, either to put down Manx abroad who over-sentimentalise the Island ('there's gold on the cushags there') or conversely for those who compare the Island unfavourably to places abroad.

Medicinal herbs

It is not difficult to understand the lasting popularity of herbal medicine on the Isle of Man. In medieval times the Lords of Man made it difficult for commoners to travel (to seek medical help, for example), and the Island was particularly late in acquiring a resident doctor. Even when trained doctors eventually came to these shores, many country folk could only afford traditional medicines anyway. Hence these home-grown cures endured for much longer than they did in many other parts of the British Isles.

SOME MANX NAMES AND THEIR MEANINGS

English name	Manx name	Translation
Thrift	***Kione Jiarg***	*Red Head*
Aspen	***Chengey Mraaee***	*Woman's Tongue*
Autumn Hawkbit	***Croag Phortan***	*Crab's Claw*
Red Campion	***Blaa ny Ferrishin***	*Fairy Flower*
Giant Puffball	***Cabbyl Mooyn***	*Horse Pee*
Harebell	***Marrane Ferrish***	*Fairy Thimble*
Fumitory	***Booaghone***	*Brown Cow*
Alexanders	***Lus yn Ollie***	*Plant of the Cattle*
Navelwort	***Daa Phing***	*Two Pennies*
Fuschsia (flowers)	***Jeirnyn Yee***	*God's Tears*

The fairy flower or Red Campion. *(Vicki Harrop)*

While many people had a small cottage garden in which to grow wild flowers and introduce herbs, the chief dispenser of medicine was the 'fairy doctor'. Fairy doctors used herbs, ritual and mostly Christianised charms to help cure all manner of ills – from sick cattle to 'the evil eye' – and ailments now recognised as diseases. Fairy doctors were in common practice, even into the 20th century, though in later times they restricted their work to treating livestock and trivial complaints.

Cushag. Unwanted by landowners but still popular on the Island. *(Mike Goldie)*

The monks of Rushen Abbey at Ballasalla in the south were also great herbalists and probably grew wild flowers for medicinal purposes. Their strong international links enabled them to use and impart a huge stock of herbal knowledge on the Island.

Mayflowers

Traditionally, Beltane (May Day in English, Laa Boaldyn in Manx) is the time when fairies were at their most active, and people took precautions to defend themselves. The night before Beltane (May Eve), flowers and rushes were strewn across doors and entrances to protect house and home. These were normally yellow flowers (which fairies avoided) including primrose (*Primula vulgaris*) and the plant that is most associated with the tradition – marsh marigold (*Caltha palustris*).

Curiously, the pink-flowered lady's smock (*Cardamine pratensis*) is also called mayflower on the Island. Marsh marigold grows like an oversized buttercup in waterlogged soils, in woodland as well as pasture. It can survive in pasture because cattle seem to avoid it, but many of its former haunts have been drained and ploughed. One of the best places to see it now is at Port Cornaa, where it forms a golden carpet under the riverside woodland. Cultivated marsh marigolds still make good cut flowers, though the rain of golden petals will annoy tidy housekeepers.

Cottage gardens

Many cottages had a small outside area in which to grow useful herbs, and a large number of flowers were introduced from locations off Island. One was sweet cicely (*Myrrhis odorata*), or myrrh as it is locally known – used as a sweetener for rhubarb and gooseberries and also reputed to flower on Old Christmas Eve (4th January).

Many cottage herbs have 'escaped' into the wild and mixed with the native flora. Alexanders (*Smyrnium olusatrum*) was originally introduced as a vegetable (used and grown much like celery) and as a medicinal herb, but now it has colonised miles of road verge and dominates it in spring.

Other common plants grown were the deadly poison monkshood (*Aconitum napellus*) and herbs more familiar in herb gardens today, such as mint (*Mentha*

Marsh Marigold (or Blughtyn in Manx) is a relative of the buttercup.

spp.), rosemary (*Rosmarinus officinalis*), tansy (*Tanacetum vulgare*) and sage (*Salvia spp.*). Wild flowers that were useful but not already growing locally would also have featured in these cottage gardens. Sea kale (*Crambe maritima*), a tasty leaf vegetable found only on certain beaches, is a good example. Keen gardeners valued it highly and frequently grew it as a present, though it was not always gratefully received.

To many Manx people, the most significant wild flower in any cottage garden was (and still is) one which was introduced to the Island. Vervain (*Verbena officinalis*) is commonly known as 'yn lus' or 'the herb' or 'she vervain'. Desirable though it is, its procurement is somewhat tricky. It can be received only as a gift from someone of the opposite sex, and though hints can be dropped it can never be asked for directly. On the other hand, stealing the herb does not induce bad luck. Indeed, the plant is noted for the power of its magic – protecting against bad luck and evil.

This magic could be harnessed by drinking tea made from the leaves, though by far the most common method was to sew dried stem into clothing, particularly undergarments – a very important travel precaution for the personal safety of anyone going away from the Island. The herb could also be sewn into fishing nets. Another plant which possessed such powers, and was similarly referred to as 'the herb' or 'he-vervain', was motherwort (*Leonurus cardiaca*).

In later times cottage gardens started to become more decorative and plants of purely ornamental value were grown. Popular plants were eglantine (*Rosa rubiginosa*) or sweet briar, grown for its apple-scented leaves, and of course the Manx fuchsia (*Fuchsia magellanica*) and Manx palm (*Cordyline australis*).

Cregneash

This lovely village of whitewashed thatched cottages in the Island's south-west is largely owned and run by Manx National Heritage as a folk museum, and one of its attractions is that you can still see traditional Manx cottage gardens here.

In these small walled gardens you can find herbs, vegetables and fruit plants growing together as was the way for hundreds of years. The cottages were the homes of 19th-century crofters and the village was the last place on the Island

Vervain or 'the herb'. *(John Callister)*

A cottage garden in Cregneash with traditional 'bink' (stone seat). *(Cilla Platt)*

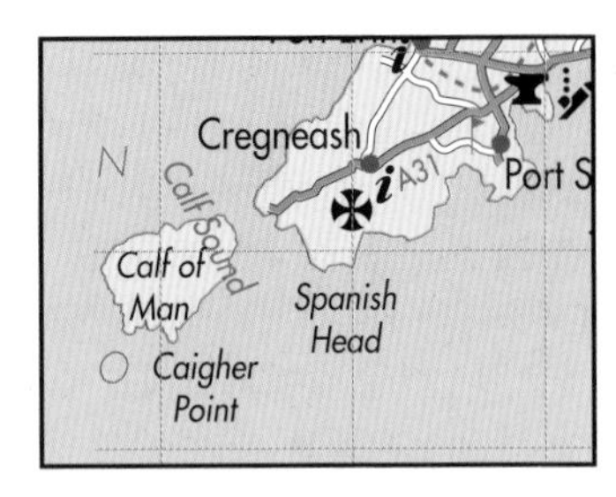

where this way of life, and the Manx language, survived. In summer months there are demonstrations of old everyday crofting skills, including cookery and the dyeing and spinning of wool from Manx Loaghtan sheep.

Preserving traditional Manx farming methods is another important aspect of this Manx National Heritage site, and the farmland around the village is managed using horsedrawn ploughs and old-fashioned crop varieties. It is easy to see why, in recent times, Cregneash has become a popular filming location for television and cinema.

The farm around Cregneash village is managed along traditional lines, allowing wild flowers to flourish. (*Cilla Platt*)

Bollan Bane.

Primroses in Malew churchyard. *(Ian Costain)*

Jough

Jough is a Manx herb beer which was widely produced in village breweries and homes. Sadly, the village brewery and the herb beer tradition are long gone, but at one time these beers were a staple drink on the Island. They were brewed in the same way as any other beer, except that local wild flowers and not hops (*Humulus lupulus*) were used to bitter the drink.

It is probable that recipes were dependent on local tradition and availability, but two plants in common use are most likely to have been ground ivy or ale hoof (*Glechoma hederacea*), which is a pungent relative of the dead nettle, and

bollan bane (mugwort). Other additions are said to have been nettles, yarrow, wild carrot, centaury (*Centaurium erythraea*), vervain, St John's-wort (*Hypericum spp.*), white horehound (*Marrubium vulgare*), bog myrtle, bogbean (*Menyanthes trifoliata*) and even hops, although the list of plants historically added to jough is in all probability much longer still.

The brewing of jough had a late illicit resurgence when Methodism became popular on the Island, and in some places virtual prohibition conditions prevailed.

Bollan Bane and Tynwald Day

On St John's Eve, the Manx parliament holds an open-air session at Tynwald

Hill in St John's village. This has become the Island's national day (July 5th, unless this falls on a weekend). Originally a Midsummer Fair (held 21st June), the occasion was changed to the feast of St John's by the Church to Christianise the tradition.

However, while St John's Day is normally celebrated with the St John's-wort flower, the common species of this plant is absent from the Isle of Man – which is why bollan bane (mugwort) is, and probably always was, the plant traditionally worn at Tynwald. It shares many of the magical qualities of St John's-wort (protecting from harm) and is also the traditional Scandinavian plant worn as a sign of loyalty to the monarch.

Bollan bane is a perennial wild flower with silver spicy-scented foliage and it grows on disturbed ground such as shingle beaches and roadsides. While handsome in spring the plant has undistinguished flowers and becomes tatty by mid-summer. Picking bits of the plant for Tynwald Day is unlikely to harm it, but it will go limp soon after picking so it is advisable to wear it so that it hangs down.

Important trees and shrubs

Many trees on the Island are said to have special qualities. Ash *(Fraxinus excelsior)*, or unjin in Manx, was regarded by the Vikings as possessing magical properties, and they referred to one ash tree as Yggdrasil or tree of life as it was said to have branches extending over the world. To the Manx the tree is associated with ash wells (chibbyr unjin), where it offers protection and purity to the well.

Hawthorn (*Crataegus monogyna*) is said to have had similar properties, though fairies have been known to hide in them. Writing your wishes on rags and tying them to hawthorn trees which 'guarded' wells supposedly made them come true.

Elder (*Sambucus nigra*), or tramman in Manx, is also very important in folklore. Its berries and flowers have traditional culinary and medicinal purposes, and the tree keeps witches away. Moreover, because fairies live below them, it is extremely unlucky to cut an elder down. This fairy belief is supported by the idea that the fungus which grows exclusively on elder (called Jew's ears across the

Rowan, a small flowering tree with red berries and a good autumn colour, is both suitable and popular for small gardens.

Harebell. *(Ian Costain)*

British Isles but known on the Island as fairy lugs) is the fairies' way of eavesdropping while they go underground. A sprig of elder could be hidden by a girl in her bosom and would mean that the first man she met would be her future husband. An additional benefit was that a lotion made from the flowers would supposedly make a girl beautiful by removing or fading her freckles.

Rowan (*Sorbus aucuparia*), or cuirn in Manx, has similar magical properties to elder. Crosses (crosh cuirn or St Bridget's cross) were made from snapped-off rowan twigs and fastened with wool snagged on briars (but never barbed wire). The cross was hung on or over the door on May Day and thereby protected the house for twelve months. Sometimes such crosses were tied to the tails of cattle to protect them too. On a more practical level, rowan berries make a popular jelly to accompany poultry and game – but you have to be quick off the mark to pick them, as blackbirds, thrushes and other birds are keen on them too.

As in much of Europe, traditional Christmas festivities have long been celebrated with home and church decorations of holly (*Ilex aquifolium*) and ivy (*Hedera helix*) – or hollin and hibbin as the Manx say. Some of it would be dried and kept until Shrove Tuesday and then burnt to cook pancakes.

Burning was also a tradition at Beltane festivals, when common gorse (*Ulex europaeus*) and Western gorse (*Ulex gallii*) were set aflame to purge the hedges of witches and fairies. Livestock were then driven between the two fires to give them additional protection.

Fairy flowers

Fairies have their favourite plants – of course! And none more so than red campion, known on the Island as the fairy flower (blaa ny ferrishin). This is a common plant of shady, damp sod hedges and woodlands, flowering en masse throughout late spring and often having a second showing of its pretty pink flowers in autumn. Greater stitchwort (*Stellaria holostea*), which grows among red campion, is called fairy's net in Manx (lieen ny ferrishin).

In parts of the south of the Island the term fairy flower is also applied to white-flowered sea campion, with red campion known as pink campion. Fairies are rather vindictive and troublesome creatures so it is quite unlucky to pick fairy

Greater stitchwort. *(Barbara Spiers)*

flowers and bring them indoors.

Another plant loved by fairies is harebell (*Campanula rotundifolia*), also called fairy's thimble. Harebell is a delicate plant of infertile dry grassland, so is often found on sod hedges and sea cliffs, sometimes in large drifts. It is strange that such a well-regarded plant today had a very poor reputation traditionally, associated with evil and haunts of fairies and witches.

The delicate look of this plant belies the fact that the tough stems will survive any gale and produce flowers all the way into October. Harebell found on the Island is different from most British varieties in that it has noticeably bigger flowers. It belongs to the western race of this species of harebell found in Ireland, Cornwall and other scattered localities.

Folklore for the future

In the passing of the last 100 years, wild flowers have gone from being an integral and essential part of life to becoming a decorative cloth for the countryside and a reminder of past but quaint customs.

This is not to say that they are no longer important to people – just that our relationship with them is no longer dictated by need, but by an appreciation of their importance to wildlife, decoration and their place in history. The significance of wild flowers is now recognised in the modern unromantic terms of bio-diversity and quality of life.

The flower folklore we are making for the future will revolve around our battles to save these unassuming plants from extinction and seeing their conservation as part of a strategy for maintaining an Island – indeed a planet – on which we are all still very dependent.

Wild flowers on farms

Farmland covers most of the lowland areas of the Isle of Man. It is dominated by a mix of arable crops, mostly of wheat and barley, and grass for cows and sheep.

Agriculture has been important on the Island for thousands of years and many wild flowers have found a home in fields and their boundaries. But in the

Flowering pasture. *(Mike Goldie)*

A relative of dandelion, cat's-ear, thrives in pastures and mown grass, where it awaits a chance to flower and seed. *(Ian Costain)*

past 60 years the fortunes of Manx wild flowers have suffered more on farmland than anywhere else on the Island.

Over this period there has been an industrialisation of agriculture, the nation seeking to become more self-sufficient and eliminate any possible spectre of famine. Farmers have sought mastery over all things natural and unpredictable, as they have completely changed the way they work. In have come pesticides, artificial fertilisers, herbicides and wire fences; out have gone wetlands, flowering meadows and many sod hedges.

Fortunately, these changes to the Island's traditional diverse farming have not damaged the landscape and its habitats as badly as new farming techniques have done in other parts of the British Isles. Evidence of Manx farms as they used to be is still apparent from nature reserves, unsprayed crops and the many surviving sod hedges.

Cornfield annuals, grown today for the landscape value. *(DOT&L)*

Cornfield annuals

Thousands of years ago when farmers first tilled the land, they created open, well-lit and cultivated conditions that few of the Manx wild flowers of the time would have been able to exploit.

These farmers also brought bags of seed to sow their first crops – and hitching a ride in the bags were cornfield annual weeds, originating from the Middle East, the Mediterranean and possibly even further afield. Inevitably, the weeds like the seeds were spread by the Island's Stone Age farmers. It is thanks to this that some of the most loved and familiar wild flowers, such as poppies *(Papaver spp.)*, wild pansies (*Viola arvensis*) and corn marigolds (*Chrysanthemum segetum*), exist on the Isle of Man today.

These wild flowers were a curse to farmers, competing with crops and resulting in a tangle of vegetation which complicated harvesting. But wild flowers support lots of insect life which in turn attracts corncrakes (*Crex crex*), skylarks (*Alauda arvensis*) and a wealth of other birds. Before farmers had access to chemical herbicides the only method of control was to remove weeds by hand, hoe or till – a never-ending battle farmers were never going to win.

The advent of chemicals that kill weeds but leave the crop undamaged has tilted the scales in farmers' favour fairly radically, but in field margins and corners that have been missed by sprayers you can find an interesting assortment of wild flowers. Many of these plants, such as fumitory (*Fumaria spp.*), common hemp nettle (*Galeopsis tetrahit*), corn spurrey (*Spergula arvensis*) and scarlet pimpernel (*Anagallis arvensis*), are real beauties and still common – though very easily missed unless you are willing to get down on hands and knees to look for them.

A recent trend in gardens is to grow poppies, cornflowers (*Centaurea cyanus*) and some of the showier cornfield annuals, but there are many pretty though less familiar plants you could adopt too.

Corn Marigold

While fields of poppies may never again be a familiar sight in the countryside, there is one showy cornfield annual that is occasionally numerous

John Crellin's Meadow, St Jude's. A meadow dominated by whorled caraway (*Carum verticillatum*), a plant found in profusion on a few Manx sites but rarely seen elsewhere in the British Isles.

enough to be a troublesome weed to farmers. Corn marigold, a plant still common in the wetter climate of the western British Isles, has the brightest yellow flowers from May onwards (it is considered to be one of the mayflowers of Beltane), and while farmers think of it as a pest its ability to paint a field golden yellow makes it a beautiful attraction for everyone else.

Pasture

The majority of Manx farmland is composed of pasture for cows, sheep, horses and occasionally pigs and poultry. Before farmers arrived, grassland had been restricted to small natural forest glades grazed by deer and other large wild creatures. The first practice that could be described as farming would have been concerted efforts to domesticate these wild herds and to manage and enlarge natural glades.

Today the process is complete: livestock is docile, fat and very numerous and the glades have expanded to surround the few fragments of remaining woodland. Much of the pasture land has been ploughed, drained, fertilised and resown with fast-growing grasses and clovers, leaving little or no room for wild flowers, though there are still large areas too steep, rocky or wet to be improved for agriculture.

At first glance these pastures do not look good for wild flowers; grazing livestock nibble off any flower that dares stick its head up over the grass. If, however, a field is relieved of livestock for a few weeks in summer, a startling transformation takes place. From tiny daisies (*Bellis perennis*) to harebell and cat's-ear (*Hypochoeris radicata*), a large number and variety of wild flowers spring into colourful life. Amazingly, many of these plants can survive grazing for years without ever flowering, awaiting a short respite in which to flower and set seed.

Sown as a wild flower meadow for conservation in the 1980s, this meadow in the north of the Island is dominated by ox-eye daisy.

White-flowered pignut, commonly found with buttercups in grassland.

Lady's smock, which is also commonly known as cuckoo flower and milk maids, here on the Isle of Man.

It could be that some of these pastures have been grazed in the same way for thousands of years, their locations often rendering them safe from any future radical change.

Lady's Smock and Garey

A plant of meadows and garey (a Manx term for wet pasture), lady's smock is often found where rushes grow. This pretty pink flower remains a common sight on the Island, reflecting the amount of garey that has survived. As these pastures are often not grazed until late spring the plants get a chance to flower. Lady's smock actually benefits from cattle grazing, since one of its chief methods of reproduction is by leaf cuttings. Cow hooves break off leaves which are then walked to a new site and conveniently pressed into the ground to produce new plants.

Orange-tip butterfly feeding on bluebell. Only males have the orange tips to their wings; females are all white. *(Barbara Spiers)*

Orange-tip butterfly (*Anthocharis cardamines*) is an insect of mid spring, males having distinctive orange tips to their wings. Lady's smock is the caterpillar's favourite food plant and these little butterflies will often be seen flitting around wet pastures.

Flowering hay meadows

The necessity to feed stock in winter months when plants have stopped growing brought about the development of haymaking. It was found that if grass was cut and dried in early summer its nutritional value was preserved for winter.

Meadows have been managed for over a thousand years since, much to the liking of a variety of wild flower species. There would have been a time when large areas were devoted to making hay and a single meadow could be home to over 100 species of wild flower, each providing different nutrients and ensuring that animals fed on the hay received a varied and healthy winter diet.

However, farmers found that they could improve their yields by ploughing out the flowering meadows and replacing them with single varieties of fast-growing grass. Then they discovered that they could pickle the grass to make silage and get 2-3 crops instead of one. In England it has been found that 98% of flowering meadows have disappeared, and unfortunately the Isle of Man has suffered nearly the same loss.

The true flowering hay meadow – one of the great treasures of the countryside – is now a rare sight and a subtle pleasure. Flowers create pale drifts and grasses tone down the colour. No two meadows are the same, some dominated by the yellow of meadow buttercup (*Ranunculus acris*) or the white of ox-eye daisy (*Leucanthemum vulgare*). Around the Ballaugh Curragh, in the north of the Island, meadows are turned pink by thousands of orchids. Many meadows grade from one colour to another during the course of the season and every season is different from any other.

Making hay at Close Sartfield Nature Reserve.

Yellow rattle in flower. *(Barbara Spiers)*

Yellow rattle seed pods. *(Barbara Spiers)*

An orchid meadow at Close Sartfield Nature Reserve. *(DOT&L)*

The key to flowering meadows is the annual removal of hay, taking with it a year's accumulated nutrients and thereby preventing grasses from becoming vigorous enough to swamp the wild flowers. To further hamper meadow grasses, some flowering plants have become grass parasites, their roots taking a cut of the nutrients found by the grass. In places they are so successful that areas of grass are killed off completely. The most common of these plants are yellow rattle (*Rhinanthus minor*) and eyebright (*Euphrasia spp.*) – closely related annuals.

Another factor that helps a good flowering meadow along is being grazed in late summer through to late winter (aftermath grazing). This creates gaps in the turf for plants to germinate and conveniently treads in the seed dropped from hay.

Close Sartfield

Purchased in 1987 and now over 30 acres in extent, this is the flagship nature reserve of Manx Wildlife Trust. It is on the fringes of the Ballaugh Curragh and shares with it a high water table and fairly poor acidic soils.

The site comprises six fields, largely nestled within and separated by a willow woodland (curragh). The fields are managed in the traditional way by Manx Wildlife Trust as meadows for flora, especially orchids. The method employed was once commonplace on the Island for large areas of enclosed farmland. The site is left to flower in spring and early summer, when the hay is cut, dried and removed from site to be stored for winter stock feed. In November to March, Manx Loaghtan sheep (the native breed) graze the meadows and create a short turf ready to grow the following spring. Hay is cut as late as possible to allow the orchids to set seed.

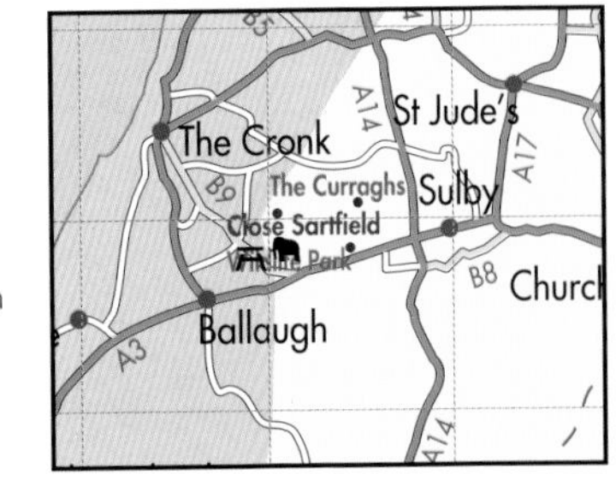

The site looks untouched by modern farming, but this is deceptive. Many of the flower-rich meadows were cultivated for potatoes and turnips as late as the 1980s, and the transformation to the colourful meadows you can see today is down to enlightened

Reserves manager Tricia Sayle giving a guided walk.

management practices.

The reserve is worthy of a visit at any time of year but in early June (around the time of the TT motorcycle racing festival) the orchids are at their best. The meadows where they grow in such profusion become a hazy pink – a spectacle unrivalled anywhere in Western Europe – and guided orchid walks are an annual event enjoyed by hundreds of people. There are now over 100,000 orchids on the reserve and yearly monitoring shows that the number is increasing. And Close Sartfield is just one of many meadows managed by Manx Wildlife Trust in the Curragh area.

Cashtal yn Ard. *(Miles Cowsill - Lily Publications)*

In late summer knapweed will flower for weeks. *(Barbara Spiers)*

European gorse in full flower. *(Linda Moore)*

Wild flowers on Fisher's Hill, Castletown. *(Mike Goldie)*

Manx sod hedges

A Manx sod hedge is a tall bank built of soil and turf and designed to keep livestock in or out. Boundaries similar to this are found in Devon, Cornwall and other parts of western Britain where higher-than-average rainfall allows vegetation to survive the summer.

Most early sod hedges were temporary structures built in autumn and ploughed back in come spring. They have in time become more permanent structures and many surviving today are hundreds of years old.

The first sod hedges were six feet high and the same at the base, with turf cut from the adjacent land to create a ditch 18 inches deep either side of the bank. They were built with sods of turf laid like bricks, making two outer walls and a core filled with stone and compacted soil. Recently-built sod hedges show that it takes decades for the outer vegetation to mesh and take on the fine grassy look of the mature sod hedge complete

Sod hedges on rich red sandstone, Peel.
(Watercolour by Cheryl Cousins)

with established wild flowers.

With some hedges, the bottom third or more is built of stone with a soil core and a pure sod hedge on top. Over the years, many older hedges have been repaired in a manner reflecting the time of the repair and the character of the builder. Storms and falling trees are common causes of collapse, and short lengths of hedge may boast a dozen different building styles.

Similarly, stone reflects local availability. In the Peel area, for example, the stone is a warm red; close to rivers, rounded stones are used; in the mountains you will find slate; and around Castletown, block limestone. Modern stone-based sod hedges are normally quarried slate and have a distinctive dark but not unpleasant look.

Poppies overlooking Port St Mary. *(Mike Goldie)*

Sheepsbit, a small wild flower which brightens up sod hedges in early summer.

Sod hedges on Manx hills have heathers on the top grading to marsh plants below. *(Watercolour by Cheryl Cousins)*

Most sod hedges are capped with some sort of shrub or tree – occasionally mature ash and elm (*Ulmus glabra*) or hawthorn. Near human habitation, fuchsia or daisy bush (*Olearia x haastii*) are planted, but by far the most common top to any sod hedge is European gorse, which was adopted by farmers after its introduction to the Island. Gorse makes a thick low hedge which can survive any wind right up to the sea. Such a perfect windbreak gives shelter to livestock in cold winter gales. As an evergreen, gorse could also be used as winter feed, farmers defeating its sharp prickles by constructing water-powered mills to turn it into a more palatable form. The remains of these Island mills can be seen today at places such as Ballaskella in Sulby. Gorse flowers all through the year, peaking in late winter. The scent is of sweet coconut and provides a fragrant treat for early walkers.

With wild flowers being managed out of existence in many farm fields, sod hedges have become their last stronghold. The hedges' structure makes them particularly suitable, the dry tops good for plants such as harebell, wild thyme and sheepsbit. The shady lower bank is where primroses, common sorrel (*Rumex acetosa*) and fairy flower (red campion) thrive, and below this level the damp ditch houses plants such as common valerian (*Valeriana officinalis*) and meadowsweet.

As for maintenance, sod hedges need a trimming once or twice a year to prevent gorse, bramble (*Rubus fruticosus*) and tussocky grasses taking over. By and large, Manx sod hedges remain in good shape thanks to farmers and the Department of Transport all doing their best to help promote the survival of hedge flora.

Sod hedges around Castletown have a limestone flora. *(Watercolour by Cheryl Cousins)*

Moor, mountain and heath

A third or more of the Island is considered to be upland – unenclosed open tracts of land. Except for planted areas of conifers, the upland is virtually treeless, the soil is poor, the rainfall is high, and wind speeds are greater than in low-lying areas.

In centuries past, when there was a cover of trees, the soils would have been fairly fertile, but once Bronze Age and Iron Age people cleared the land the nutrients leached out of the ground and much of the topsoil washed away. This ancient example of ecological destruction created the uplands as they are today – a landscape of international conservation importance and almost unique to the British Isles.

The bleak uplands were seen by many in the past two hundred years as a wet desert waiting to be improved and used productively. Over time a great deal of effort has gone into enclosing upland areas to turn them into fertile pasture (intack) or conifer plantations, but much of the land has since reverted back to moor and the remains of old boundaries are all that testify to the past efforts of farmers. Some of the land carved from the heath was so poor and thin that soil had to be mounded up in rows (lazy beds) to get enough for crops to grow in.

Between 1885 and 1890, 71% of the Island was agriculturally-improved land. The figure is now less than 50% – proof of the capacity of heath to recolonise on mountain landscape. Currently the gains and losses of upland are cancelling

Gorse growing alongside ruins of old industry. *(Ian Costain)*

The flower of heather (ling) is a welcome feast for bees. *(Mike Goldie)*

each other out, with some farmers keen to clear, plough and resow and others leaving the most marginal areas for mountain vegetation to recolonise. Heather seed can lay dormant in the ground for over 50 years, biding its time and colonising when the opportunity arises.

Manx heath

Heathland is defined as any vegetation dominated by short shrubs of the heather family, of which heather (*Calluna vulgaris*), or ling, and the prettier bell heather (*Erica cinerea*) are the Island's main species.

Bell heather tends to dominate on the thinnest, driest soils and ling can even survive on waterlogged ground. The other large component of much Manx heath is western gorse, a short relative of European gorse. It flowers in late summer at the same time as heather, creating an unforgettable patchwork of yellow and purple.

A third type of heather, the cross-leaved heath (*Erica tetralix*) has pale pink flowers and can be found in the wettest ground. Bilberry (*Vaccinium myrtillus*) or blaeberry is related to heather and tends to dominate in areas where no sheep graze or in shady conditions. It is quite prolific in parts, and the tradition on 1st August was for people to climb the mountains to pick tasty blue bilberry fruit, and engage in other fruitier pastimes.

Peak flowering time for heath is mid-August to mid-September. At this time of year the mountains are magically transformed from austere but impressive bleakness to a mauve and yellow carpet alive with bees and hoverflies flocking to the nectar event of the year. The scent can only be described as that of summer.

As well as shrubs, many other flowering plants grow alongside the heather. The most common of these is tormentil (*Potentilla erecta*), a plant whose small yellow flowers bloom from mid-spring to late summer. Another common plant is heath bedstraw (*Galium saxatile*), which climbs over heather in early summer and cloaks it white. Lichen, moss and fungi are more noticeable in heathland than in other habitats, and all add to the interest if you look closely.

As well as low-intensity grazing of sheep, many Manx heaths (particularly in

Manx heath – an area of vegetation dominated by short shrubs of the heather family. *(Ian Costain)*

Looking towards Douglas from Beinn-y-Phott. ***(Miles Cowsill - Lily Publications)***

Sulby Glen. *(Miles Cowsill - Lily Publications)*

the south) undergo small controlled burns in winter to regenerate the heather and lower the risk of major uncontrolled wild fires in summer. These small winter burns do not kill the roots or seeds of most heathland plants; within a year or two they recover, providing more palatable grazing for the sheep that roam these uplands. The mix of young and old heather is also necessary for red grouse (*Lagopus lagopus*), a bird which has struggled for a long time to survive in the Isle of Man and is dependent on the upland heaths to raise its young. The 'pots' (as these burns are known) are mainly carried out for grouse management by the Manx Game Preservation Society, which for many years has worked tirelessly to conserve these birds. Many rarer upland wild flowers such as cowberry (*Vaccinium vitis-idaea*) are less tolerant of fire and only found outside areas which are regularly burnt.

One of the main threats to upland heath is overgrazing – a problem which has destroyed tens of thousands of acres of heathland in the British Isles and left behind a dull vegetation of matgrass. On the Isle of Man overgrazing is not such a problem, but the northern range does not have quite the same beautiful carpet of heather as around the southern hills because there is less burning and more grazing. These extensive areas of grass are valued by some birds but are a poor habitat for flowering plants.

Other threats to heathland include invasion of bracken fern (*Pteridium aquilinum*) and European gorse, both of which are taller plants that swamp the heath. They can become very invasive after fire, so the precise placing of controlled burns is important. In the past bracken has had a number of very practical uses – as animal bedding, as packing material for fragile goods, and was burnt for its pure ash, which was an ingredient in glass making. Pigs and cattle that once roamed the uplands alongside sheep helped control bracken by trampling its fronds and unearthing its roots. But with these traditional 'measures' all now extinct, bracken has been spreading to its heart's content. This has been good for bluebells and other plants which often colonise underneath dominant bracken, and parts of the uplands such as Glen Rushen now display a carpet of bluebells in spring before the bracken fronds grow up.

As heathland gets closer to the sea, many other plants mix in and thrift and

Lousewort, a relative of yellow rattle. *(Barbara Spiers)*

harebells can often be seen growing alongside heather. Rabbits are more frequent at lower altitudes and create small lawns of closely-cropped grass and other areas of wild flowers. Most of the rocky coast has heathland nearby, except around the limestone areas of the south-east – soils on which heather won't survive. These maritime heaths have a more amenable climate and are a better habitat for insects such as green tiger beetle and solitary wasps and bees.

Eary Cushlin

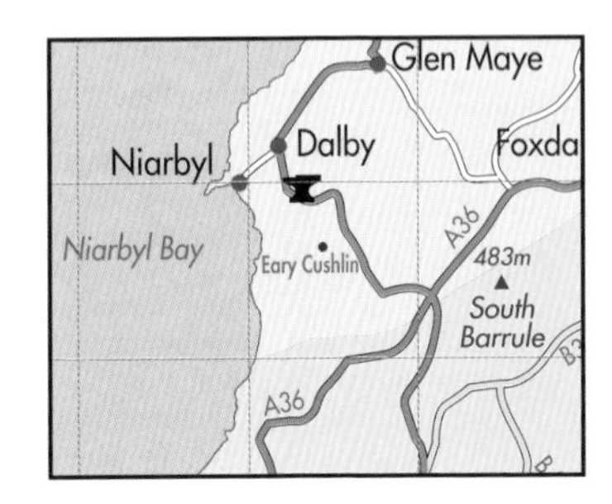

Part of the Island's spectacular south-west coastline, Eary Cushlin is owned and managed by Manx National Heritage. The site is a mix of bog, dry mountain heath, acid grassland and bracken land running into cliffs and the sea. The mountain heath is frequently burnt and the site is grazed by sheep.

At the centre is an old farmhouse, now a hostel and field study centre, and around this you can see the remains of an old field system. The sod hedges are partly collapsed and livestock roam freely over the area, much of which is grassland. In late summer harebells are a particularly colourful feature. Heather grows freely among the grass and gorse is slowly invading from the edges. The sheep grazing will slow the heather's progress, but in time it is likely that much of the old field system will return to heather, gorse and bracken.

Small streams run through Eary Cushlin, creating corridors of rush and other wetland plants such as lesser spearwort (*Ranunculus flammula*), a relative of buttercup, and lousewort (*Pedicularis sylvatica*), a pink-flowered relative of yellow rattle. The largest stream cascades from the cliffs into the sea at Gob yn Ushtey, though this impressive sight is difficult to see from land.

Bog asphodel flower. ***(Barbara Spiers)***

Sundew.

Acid bogs

Where mountain land is poorly drained, heathland gives way to acid bog. This is a wetland habitat unlike that of any lowland area; instead of big, lush vegetation, with conspicuous flowers, an acid bog is much more subdued.

The soils of a bog are the peaty remains of plants – semi-decomposed matter, centuries old, which has been preserved in the cold, waterlogged acid conditions. Peat can preserve a record of the past for thousands of years. The remains of prehistoric forest trees have been found at the bottom of bogs, and pollen in peat reveals much about the vegetation since the end of the last ice age. It tells us, for example, that trees such as Scots pine (now only native to the Highlands of Scotland) once flourished here for several millennia, and also furnishes a great deal more knowledge about the forests and plants that inhabited the landscape so long ago – including their age, how quickly they grew, their distribution and other illuminating information.

On the Isle of Man the depth of peat is normally restricted because for so long it has been dug and dried as fuel for fires. Before coal was commonly imported, peat was the Island's main source of heating fuel. Peat forms slowly, so once dug it can take hundreds or thousands of years to reform sufficiently to be dug again. The ash from peat fires was also important as a fertiliser for lowland fields, and a large amount of peat was dug for this purpose, especially in the southern hills, resulting in permanent ecological damage to the area.

Peat bogs are rarely interfered with, as sheep will avoid them and they are too wet for fires to burn. People also tend to stay clear as the deep peaty mud is unpleasant to try and cross. This is fortunate. Not only are acid bogs very fragile ecosystems, easily damaged because the soil has no real structure; they also take decades to recover from any kind of abuse.

Only very specialised plants grow in a bog. In the wettest areas sphagnum moss dominates, but where water lies just below the surface a greater variety of plants occur. The most noticeable of these are cotton grass and bog asphodel (*Narthecium ossifragum*), which together produce swathes of white and yellow. Other plants such as cross-leaved heath, heath spotted orchid (*Dactylorhiza*

Deer grass in winter.

maculata) and lousewort are found dotted around the bog. Few bog plants grow tall, as wet structureless soil offers little anchorage for roots and the wind would soon blow them over. Where the soil is less acid an occasional willow tree may stick out, but sheep will then have a reason to cross the mire to get at it.

The soil of bogs is so poor that some plants supplement their diet by catching insects. Round-leaved sundew (*Drosera rotundifolia*) and common butterwort (*Pinguicula vulgaris*) have sticky leaves to catch and digest insects. These small, uncommon and local bog plants can be seen on wet rocks and bare ground. A stranger plant still is bladderwort (*Utricularia spp.*). Found rarely in wet pools and ditches in the Ballaugh Curragh, this plant has rows of water-filled sacs in which it traps and digests water fleas and other small water life.

Mountain grasses

Cotton grass may be instantly noticeable and recognisable, but many upland grasses are more subtle; rather than grow in large blocks, individual tussocks

Deer grass in summer.

become features of the habitat. In wet upland conditions, rushes (with rounded leaves) and sedges (with leaves which are ribbed, often M-shaped and stems that are triangular in cross-section) tend to be as common as the other grasses.

The most attractive is probably deer grass (*Trichoporum cespitosum*) – a rush which grows to about ankle height and is fairly common in acid bogs and their fringes. Each tussock produces a dome of lush green summer grass, changing in colour by late autumn to a unique dark brown. Tussocks keep their structure until fresh growth starts in spring.

Purple moor grass (*Molinia caerulea*) can grow in large drifts or as distinctive individual tussocks. The smoky-looking flower heads are as dark as their name promises. Tufted hair grass (*Deschampsia cespitosa*) blends in when among other grasses in the lowlands but becomes a distinctive feature in heath, as it grows way above all the other vegetation and has very elegant tall flower stalks. There are many other grasses worth looking for. Try finding wavy hair grass (*Deschampsia flexuosa*) or green ribbed sedge (*Carex binervis*), which look as good in winter as in summer.

Glens, forests and trees

Although the Isle of Man was once covered in forest, by the 16th century human activity had led to virtual deforestation. The recovery since then has created a lowland landscape rich in trees – along riversides, roadsides and in many gardens – but as a result of the Island's isolation and the destruction of the original forest, many woodland plants common elsewhere in the British Isles are not native here. Perhaps the most regrettable absentee is wild daffodil (*Narcissus pseudonarcissus*), a flower so abundant in the neighbouring Lake District.

Wood anemone at St John's Mill. ***(John Lamb)***

Wild garlic in spring at Bishopscourt Glen. *(Miles Cowsill - Lily Publications)*

Tree planting on the Island has been vigorous since the Victorian era and is just as popular today. This is encouraging news for anyone fearing a return to the treeless landscape of the past. In time, as the cover of mature woodland increases, birds such as woodpeckers may come to breed here and insects that rely on old trees and dead wood will colonise. Sadly, many woodland species of plant and animal are poor colonisers and will probably never come to the Island.

Glens

In every sense, Manx glens are a national treasure – not only for their natural beauty but also because the Manx government purchased many of them to form the officially-designated National Glens. A few, such as Dhoon Glen, may have contained the relics of older woodland which survived on cliff sides long after the other woodland had gone, but most of the glens were planted as naturalistic pleasure gardens by Victorian and Edwardian landscapers.

These romantic landscaped areas were mostly planted as commercial enterprises to cater for the booming tourism industry, and were profitably managed until the post-war decline of mass tourism on the Island. Many planted glens were on the routes of trains and trams to give easy access to visitors so keen to see them.

Wood sorrel looks like a clover but is unrelated and will grow in dry woodland, such as here in the bough of a tree. *(Linda Moore)*

The glens then were very different from the quiet wooded valleys they are today. Apart from the fact that the trees were much smaller, there was an extensive variety of other attractions, some of which have survived. Examples are the water-powered carousel and the boating lake in

Wild garlic grows happily alongside the steam railway. ***(Mike Goldie)***

Silverdale, and the railway, waterwheel and bandstand in Groudle Glen. There were also more formal gardens (remains of these can still be seen in Glen Helen and Laxey Glen), and even animal attractions, notably the monkey cage in Glen Helen and sealions in Groudle Glen. Other surviving features of these 'good old days' include the follies of Bishopscourt and the restaurants of Laxey Glen and Glen Helen (rebuilt after a fire). All are reminders of the heyday of the glen pleasure gardens and the abundance of follies, wooden gazebos, restaurants and cafés which this age created.

Most of the glens are now National Glens, managed and maintained by the government's Forestry Division, but others have become private gardens or are managed for the benefit of the nation by other organisations. Cooildarry, opposite Glen Wyllin, is managed for nature conservation by Manx Wildlife Trust, and Summerhill in Douglas is owned and managed by Douglas Corporation.

Where teams of gardeners once toiled and crowds of holidaymakers passed through, there now stands mature, mixed woodland. The majority of the trees are those planted in the heyday, but other trees and shrubs have sown of their own accord and the glens' 'artificial' history is harder to discern with each passing

Dhoon Glen.

year, as each mature tree falls and is replaced by one which is self-sown.

Some wild flowers are descendants of those that were planted, but most are naturally occurring – wild garlic, bluebell, wood anemone and many types of fern that form swathes of ground vegetation. The relics of the plantings normally add interest rather than look out of place. In Port Soderick Glen, salmonberry (*Rubus spectabilis* – a relative of raspberry) dominates large areas of the valley side and London pride, a popular garden plant in Victorian times, has become common in some glens.

Aside from the formal planted glen, most riversides have a rich natural growth of trees, normally where rivers are fenced off. In some parts these areas become quite wide and form ribbons of woodland through the valleys. Most riverbank trees are self-seeded ash, willow (*Salix spp.*), elm or sycamore (*Acer pseudoplatanus*) and are thick with ivy growth and a flora of wild garlic (*Allium ursinum*) and wood anemones (*Anemone nemorosa*) underneath. Many of these riverside woodlands join naturally to planted glens, thereby extending and linking the areas of natural woodland. The food and shelter provided by the trees makes them a favourite haunt of bats.

Dhoon Glen

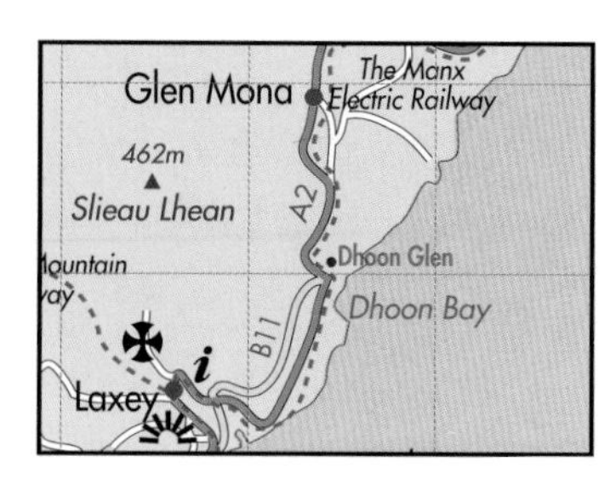

The most wild and picturesque of all Manx glens, Dhoon and the surrounding woodland make up a large chunk of semi-natural vegetation. The remoteness and steep slope of the site have protected it for thousands of years, and it has several features which although not quite unique are found in very few other places on the Island.

For example, native sessile oak and hazel are still common here, as is wood sanicle (*Sanicula europaea*), and it is also probable that there has been some woodland at Dhoon Glen since the last ice age. Alongside these rarities you will find the expected bluebells and wild garlic.

Dhoon Glen's more recent history includes a role in Victorian industry. Lead ore was mined here until the 1860s, but the mining enterprises were never profitable despite decades of work, deep shafts and enormous pumping wheels (the remains of the wheel casing still spans the glen about halfway down).

Dhoon was already a popular beauty spot long before the 1890s, but the construction of the Manx Electric Railway between Douglas and Ramsey opened the door to mass tourism to the glen. Where the train stopped there was a large hotel-restaurant and a pleasure garden, and visitors were encouraged down to Dhoon Bay by the many small paths and bridges crossing the slopes and valley bottom.

The railway still serves the glen (stopping on request) but now there is only a small café here. Where the wooden hotel once stood (it burnt down in 1932) is the glen car park, and most of the pleasure gardens are overgrown. The last path in the valley, washed away in a storm in October 2002, is now rebuilt so that visitors can still walk down to the beach via the waterfall and semi-natural semi-planted woodland.

Rosebay willowherb. One of the first colonisers of disturbed areas such as felled conifer plantations, this plant spreads itself with downy seeds that are carried miles in the wind. *(Ian Costain)*

Conifer forests

In 1883 the Manx government started planting two million (mostly conifer) trees at Archallagan, east of Foxdale. This was the first large-scale tree planting on the Island, followed over the next century by many more upland areas and sparked by the perception that these vast acres of wilderness were of very little value for anything else.

Victorian plant collectors had found dozens of fast-growing tree species from all over the world – trees that would grow rapidly even in the poorest of soils and most exposed sites. By the early 20th century one of these species came to dominate the Island's forestry plantings – Sitka spruce (*Picea sitchensis*), originally from north-west America. It is now the most common tree on the Isle of Man, planted mostly in neat rows close together. When Sitka spruce ages it is a handsome tree with a flaking bark and shaggy canopy, but most are felled for timber after 40-50 years, just as they reach maturity.

Young spruce forests are surprisingly rich in bird life but become rather lifeless as they mature. A few wild flowers manage to survive in the plantations, including hard fern (*Blechnum spicant*), bilberry and the pretty white-flowered wood sorrel (*Oxalis acetosella*). The older a plantation is, the more wild flowers will colonise as the tree canopy opens out. By the time a plantation has been thinned a few times, an interesting flora may be established. When a plantation is felled many of these woodland plants are rapidly swamped by a rush of others, such as rosebay willowherb (*Chamaerion angustifolium*), heathers and foxgloves (*Digitalis purpurea*),

Conifers in Sulby Glen.

Although little vegetation currently exists beneath these 30-year-old conifers at South Barrule Plantation, over the next 10 years wood sorrel and a few ferns should establish themselves.

Adder's tongue is an unusual fern found in old grasslands and here at South Barrule Plantation.

which become established for ten years or so before the replanted trees shade them out.

By the 1990s, opposition to more conifer plantations in the uplands prompted the development of a new forestry policy. This saved upland heaths and moor from being covered by yet more spruce trees. The existing forests are also being managed more sympathetically for nature conservation, with mature trees being left to grow and felled areas now restocked with more broadleaf trees.

Curragh

Curragh is a mixture of bog and willow-dominated low-growing woodland. Often described as scrub, this woodland habitat is in fact the most important on the Island for nature conservation. Curragh grows on waterlogged ground, unsuited to most other trees. At less than 50 years old the majority of willow ('sallie') curragh is fairly recent, reflecting a lack of interest by the farming industry in sites that are difficult to drain and use for more productive agriculture.

Bog pimpernel – a plant of curragh and wet grassland.

Native bluebell. *(Ian Costain)*

Much curragh is on deep peat soils which are permanently waterlogged. The poor structure of these soils means that if tree growth gets too heavy the soil sinks and kills the trees. Hence light willow is the only tree that can survive here. On drier areas or firmer mineral soils, other trees such as ash, holly and downy birch (*Betula pubescens*) will grow and survive to maturity among the willow, eventually shading it out and producing a more conventional 'woodland'.

Curragh is an excellent habitat for bird nesting and feeding and is home to many insects which thrive in the damp conditions. The open wet woodland environment also makes this a perfect habitat for many wild plants. In brighter areas meadowsweet, angelica (*Angelica sylvestris*) and purple loosestrife (*Lythrum salicaria*) display large visible flowers, but most of the shadier areas are dominated by grasses, ferns and honeysuckle (*Lonicera periclymenum*), though a few interesting plants such as marsh cinquefoil (*Potentilla palustris*) with its magenta flowers can also be found. With the small stagnant pools of water, the swamp effect of curragh is enhanced by the lichen and mosses dripping from the branches of the willow trees.

Where ground gives way to open water, over time an interesting transformation takes place. Bog bean (*Menyanthes trifoliata*), a water plant, grows and colonises and eventually chokes the water, allowing other plants such as willow to encroach and turn the open water into woodland, often in a matter of decades.

Bluebell under threat

Of all woodland flowers, bluebells are the most loved and still a common sight on the Island, growing in their millions in glens and shady places. Yet the bluebell is a rare sight on the European mainland and in eastern Britain is confined to scattered ancient woodland. Here in the west it rapidly colonises new areas which have the humid, sheltered conditions it requires.

In the quest for novelty, gardeners have introduced the bluebell's close relative, the Spanish bluebell (*Hyacinthoides hispanicus*). This is a bigger, faster-growing species, but what it boasts in size it lacks in elegance. Unlike their native relatives, Spanish bluebell flowers are not scented, nor do they nod gracefully,

The Broogh, Nr Braaid. *(Miles Cowsill - Lily Publications)*

Foxglove.

These 80-year-old Sitka spruce have been left to grow and become huge specimen trees. *(Miles Cowsill - Lily Publications)*

instead standing bolt upright. The native blue has maybe a one-in-a-million chance of being white-flowered, but the Spanish species is nearly 50% white or even pink, and the blue lacks the intensity of the native. None of this would be a problem but Spanish bluebells have 'escaped' from Island gardens and are flooding into the wild. The two species readily produce hybrids which share characteristics of both parents, and many native wild bluebell colonies have been seriously affected, especially around Douglas.

Veteran and specimen trees

Trees of antiquity are known as veteran trees, and tend to be those over 200 years old. Some shorter-lived trees such as birch and ash can be regarded as veteran at a much younger age, but they rarely survive long enough to become gnarled old specimens.

With the Island's history of deforestation there are few trees that fit into the veteran category. Most of the oldest trees grow in coastal areas too steep or inaccessible for sheep to get to, and are too small and stunted for people to chop down for firewood. Some of these trees grow in woodlands such as Santon Gorge and Dhoon Glen, but many others occur as single, stunted trees, often just a few feet high, around the coast. The majority of these are sessile oak (*Quercus petraea*) – the last relics of oak forest that cloaked the Island thousands of years ago.

Some veteran trees can be found in the grounds of Bishopscourt and other large old houses, put in as young trees in the 18th century when landscaped grounds were becoming very popular. The trees of the Victorian era are still technically 70 years or more away from veteran status, but many are large and maintain vigorous growth in the glens. As some of the weaker trees fall, larger specimens such as beech (*Fagus sylvatica*) in Groudle and Glen Helen, and silver fir (*Abies alba*) in Ballaglass, are giving an impressive preview of how the glen plantings will look at the end of the 21st Century.

Veteran trees are not only interesting in themselves; they are also home to a rich variety of plant, fungus and animal life. One fern, polypody, specialises in growing on the trunk and branches of old trees, the moss and detritus on the

Andrew 'Mill' Millichap collecting ash seed for the Native Oak Group.

bark providing the fern's roots with all the sustenance required. Ivy grows up old trees and in turn provides shelter to over-wintering insects and bats, which also use the tree cavities. It is only when a tree is very old that ivy becomes a problem, as the ivy's weight can help bring it down in a fierce gale.

Very old trees are often partially hollow on the inside due to the action of fungi and wood-boring insects, typically beetle and wood wasp larvae. Surprisingly, rather than harm trees, the hollow cylinder shape is every bit as strong as a solid trunk, and much lighter too.

The Native Oak Group

Native trees and shrubs have been ousted from much of the Isle of Man and left clinging to a few natural woodland cliffs and riversides. This sad fact spawned the creation of the Native Oak Group, whose aim is to grow the native trees of the Island. Rather than oak from Germany or England, trees of Manx origin can be planted, preserving the local genetic stock. These trees are better adapted to Manx conditions, and the insects that rely upon them will probably be better adapted to the trees. The Native Oak Group also grows ash, birch, elm, alder, rowan and a variety of other trees and shrubs.

Coastal habitats

The Isle of Man's 100 miles of coastline comprise high cliffs, sand dunes, salt marsh and beaches of sand and shingle, and many species of Manx wild flowers are found exclusively or mainly in these coastal habitats. They cover a wide spectrum, ranging from thrift (sea pink) and other very familiar flora to exotic-looking plants which are less well known, such as sea holly (*Eryngium maritimum*) and yellow horned-poppy (*Glaucium flavum*).

Plants adapted to coastal conditions enjoy a mild climate, where frost is rare and humidity and light levels are high. The price they pay is to endure the

Thrift grows in abundance on the Isle of Man ***(Ian Costain)***

Purple milk vetch - best seen at Scarlett. *(Linda Moore)*

Kidney vetch, very common at Scarlett, can be found in less abundantly on thin soil around most rocky coasts. ***(Barbara Spiers)***

harshest salt-laden winds and survival on cliffs, beaches and dunes that are continuously eroded, blown or washed away. Some plants, such as sea aster (*Aster tripolium*) and sea rocket (*Cakile maritima*), have evolved to survive coastal conditions, while kidney vetch (*Anthyllis vulneraria*), purple milk vetch (*Astragalus danicus*) and others grow far inland in countries south and east of the Isle of Man but can only live near the coast in this climate. Some plants occur as commonly near the coast as inland. Bird's-foot trefoil (*Lotus corniculatus*) thrives in any short turf or disturbed soil, and when growing close to the sea often has a distinctive hairy leaf to resist the salty wind.

The exposed conditions of much of the coast inhibit tree growth, so the vegetation growing here now has many similarities to that found 10,000 years ago. The coastline, however, has changed. Where the sea meets the rocky coast erosion is very slow, but from Kirk Michael to Jurby the constant pounding of waves against the loose sediments is rapidly eating away parts of the Island year by year. The speed of erosion has led to the extinction of at least one plant – strawberry clover (*Trifolium fragiferum*).

Coastal erosion at Jurby. *(Tricia Sayle)*

Sea cliffs

Much of the Isle of Man's coast is dominated by rocky shores and sea cliffs, with isolated sea stacks jutting into the sea. At the tide line few plants can survive the relentless wave action, but a closer look reveals that all the rocks are encrusted with lichen growths, from jet black to light orange to grey-green.

Over 100 species of lichen are confined to or prefer to grow near the Island's coast. Out of the reach of most waves, some plants such as thrift grow in any crevice in bare rocks. Higher up, small amounts of soil collect in crags and ledges and

Sea spleenwort – a fern restricted to rocks and caves within the splash zone of the sea.

Spring squill – a tiny spring flowering bulb found all around the coast. *(Barbara Spiers)*

Sea mayweed. *(Mike Goldie)*

any number of seaside plants can establish themselves, including sea campion, red fescue (*Festuca rubra*), thyme (*Thymus polytrichus*) and English stonecrop (*Sedum anglicum*). Further up the cliff face still, vegetation tends to give way to heathland or a maritime turf.

Where water seeps down bare rocks, ferns grow. One of the rarest is Maidenhair fern (*Adiantum capillus-veneris*). Better known as a common houseplant, this fern will not survive much frost or competition and is restricted in the wild to a few sea caves on the Island's west coast near Peel. Another species, royal fern, is associated with curragh but has a second niche habitat on sea cliffs and caves where it can be quite common, as at Douglas Head Lighthouse.

Maritime turf is a grassland dominated by red fescue grass but also rich in wild flowers such as harebell, daisy, spring squill (*Scilla verna*) and sheepsbit (*Jasione montana*). Away from the limestones of the Island's south-east, heathers grow among the grassland, which tends to give way to maritime heathland further upslope. Whilst most livestock is fenced off from the cliffs, rabbits are

Dark green fritillary – probably the most attractive of the Island's butterflies. *(Barbara Spiers)*

very common and the disturbance they cause allows plants such as sea mayweed (*Tripleurospermum maritimum*) and buckshorn plantain (*Plantago coronopus*) to flourish. On wetter ground, plants typical of inland wetlands such as meadowsweet and hemlock water dropwort (*Oenanthe crocata*) also thrive. Blackthorn (*Prunus spinosa*) is a shrub that normally grows to 4 metres or more but on the Isle of Man it occurs most commonly on the coast, where wind-pruned knee-high thickets are frequently found.

Stretches of coast are dominated by bracken, which shades out many plants, but where it is not too vigorous it allows bluebells and common dog violets (*Viola riviniana*) to survive. Violet is the food plant of the caterpillar of the dark green fritillary (*Argynnis aglaja*), a large but infrequently seen butterfly.

Saltmarsh

In most places wave action makes it impossible for plants to grow below the high tide line. However, in sheltered areas, notably the Castletown side of Langness and the mouth of the Sulby River, small areas of marsh covered by

Wood vetch looks a little like a sweet pea and is found at just one site – Glen Maye. *(Linda Moore)*

Sea aster at Langness.

most high tides support plants which have evolved to survive twice-daily flooding and a diet of saltwater. A few familiar plants – red fescue and thrift, for example – can also be seen but most plants here will not survive anywhere else but in saltmarsh. Most of these specialised plants are rushes and sedges, but in mid-summer saltmarsh is transformed by sea aster, a purple-flowered plant which can carpet large areas. The fortunes of saltmarshes fluctuate wildly. Big storms can wash them away, but equally their size and diversity can be extended by silt and seeds washed in from hundreds of miles away establishing new species.

The Ayres

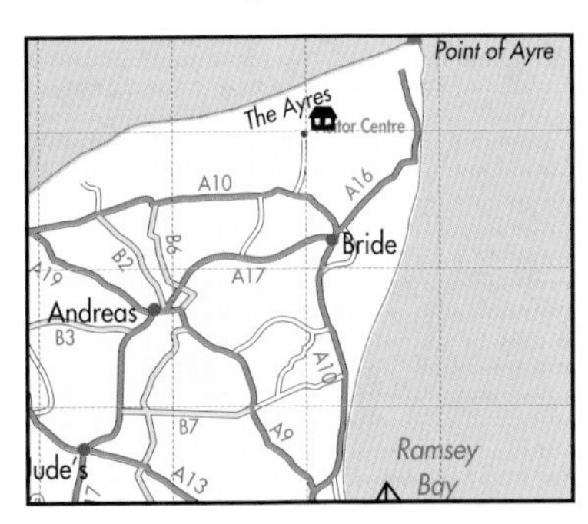

A stretch of land culminating at the extreme northern tip of the coastline, the Ayres is one of the most important and diverse wildlife sites on the Isle of Man.

The coastal side of the Ayres is dominated by sand dunes – one of

Saltmarsh at Poylldooey, Ramsey. *(Manx National Heritage)*

only two places on the Island where they occur, the other being in a small part of Castletown links. The Ayres' dunes systems are a narrow band, four and a half miles long, with sandy beach on one side and lichen heath on the other. The most noticeable plant of the dunes is marram grass (*Ammophila arenaria*) – a tough grass more commonly known on the Island as bent and for a long time used as roofing thatch for cottages. Its main function now is to bind the dunes' sand to stop it from blowing away.

When marram was cut for thatch, the dunes were neither as high nor as diverse in nature conservation terms as they are today. The sand comes from the sea cliffs eroding between Kirk Michael and Jurby. Carried by the tide, it washes on to the Ayres beach and is blown by winds on to the dunes. Every year tonnes of sand are deposited this way and the Ayres is slowly becoming larger as the dunes claim land from the sea. From 1946 to 1998, the dunes at Rue Point extended into the sea by a distance of 30 metres.

The blown sand brings with it bits of seashell, allowing lime-loving plants such as pyramidal orchid (*Anacamptis pyramidalis*) to grow in its hundreds. The seashells dissolve after a period of time and on the landward side of the dunes the sand is quite acidic. Like saltmarshes, dune systems take hundreds or thousands of years to develop but can be washed away by a single big storm. Fortunately, such extreme weather may itself only occur once every few millennia.

The vast majority of the Ayres is lichen heath. This internationally-rare type of maritime heath is heavily grazed by rabbits, causing open heather vegetation with soil too poor to allow grass to dominate. This enables the lichen that gives this vegetation its name to cover up to 70% of the heath.

Parts of the heath are dominated by the sweetly-scented burnet rose (*Rosa pimpinellifolia*), which is stunted by poor soils, wind exposure and most importantly rabbits. Among the burnet rose are other wild flowers such as sheepsbit, harebell, thyme and stonecrop, along with moss and lichen. Dune and grass areas furthest from the sea are home to autumn lady's tresses (*Spiranthes spiralis*). The Ayres is the most northerly place in the British Isles in which this orchid is found, and although in wet winters the area is prone to flooding and

Pyramidal orchid amongst marram grass on sand dunes at the Ayres. *(Manx National Heritage)*

Sea holly. *(Linda Moore)*

Burnet rose. *(Linda Moore)*

populations of this and other orchids appear to be wiped out, they seem to recover after a number of drier years. However, there is currently concern that autumn lady's tresses may have become extinct, as they were not seen at the Ayres in either 2002 or 2003.

At the eastern end of the Ayres, old sand and gravel pits have been used for decades as a landfill site for the Island and are now almost full. The site is being restored as heathland vegetation and should in time blend in with the existing heathland.

In 1996, in recognition of the importance of the Ayres for nature conservation, 632 acres of the site became the first to be designated an Area of Special Scientific Interest by the Isle of Man Government, and in 2000 the Ayres became the Island's first National Nature Reserve.

Beach flowers

Away from the seaside towns, the Island's many coves and beaches are unspoilt and undeveloped. Above the strand line beaches have a fair array of

Nastursium and callenda are garden annuals which have 'escaped' on to Castletown Bay's shingle beach, such as here at Queen's Street. *(Mike Goldie)*

Sea kale. *(Manx National Heritage)*

Sea sandwort (*Honkenya peploidies*). (*Linda Moore*)

Sea bindweed. *(Ralph Lowey)*

wild flowers, most of which would not normally get a second look, but among them are some interesting and attractive plants.

Strand line wild flowers have historically been collected as nutritious foodstuffs. The most popular was sea kale (*Crambe maritima*), but sea beet (*Bēta vulgaris subsp. maritima*), sea rocket (*Cakile maritima*) and oraches (*Atriplex spp.*) are among the edible plants commonly found. They are naturally salty with a high vitamin C content and are normally eaten boiled. The winter storms blow in large amounts of seaweed to the shores and their fertilising effect produces succulent healthy plants.

On shingle beaches the growth of plants tends to be sparse, the notable species including sea mayweed and yellow horned-poppy. At the higher, less disturbed parts of a beach, diversity increases with plants such as bird's-foot trefoil, cushag, creeping cinquefoil (*Potentilla reptans*), mugwort and tree mallow all creating a summer carpet. In winter through it's the shingle that shows through; most plants have died down or are covered in seaweed. Another feature of the higher shingle is the presence of established exotic plants – hebe (*Hebe x franciscana*), for example. This is frequently because people have simply dumped garden rubbish on the beach and some plants have taken, while in other places gardens back on to the beach and garden plants 'escape'.

The sandy beaches in the bays of Peel, Port Erin and Douglas have a sea wall at the high tide line, so no wild flowers now live there. To find undeveloped

Common storksbill. ***(Manx National Heritage)***

Hebe – a garden shrub which has 'escaped' and now grows wild on some beaches. *(Manx National Heritage)*

Common Centaury. *(Linda Moore)*

sandy beaches on the Isle of Man you have to go north, to the Ayres and Ramsey Bay, although small areas of sand can also be found in Castletown Bay. Sandy beaches can sustain most wild flowers common to shingle beaches, but also support many more which are unique to the habitat. Beach tourists walking barefoot in the sandy vegetation soon become familiar with saltwort (*Salsola kali*), as this low-growing annual is a mean prickly plant. Another prickly species is handsome sea holly (*Eryngium maritimum*), which along with sea bindweed (*Calystegia soldanella*) and sea spurge (*Euphorbia paralias*) are the prettiest of the sandy shore plants. They are all still common around Ramsey Bay and the Ayres.

The Isle of Man Cabbage (*Coincya monensis subsp. monensis*)

This plant was first named on the Isle of Man in the 1600s but has since been found between the west coast of Scotland and Devon. A short-lived perennial or annual, it is confined to sandy shores and can be common. As a

Isle of Man cabbage, Ramsey Bay. *(Linda Moore)*

relative of the cabbage it makes a tasty treat for rabbits.

Once found around Douglas and Peel – haunts which are now built over – Isle of Man cabbage is today confined to the north. It grows well in Ramsey Bay, but over the years rabbits have greatly reduced the cabbage's population at the Ayres. Though not the most attractive of plants, it is fondly regarded as the only wild flower named after the Island.

Dame's violet. Once a herb in cottage gardens, this is now found on Manx sod hedges such as here on the Ballamodha Straight.

Exotics and invaders

Wave after wave of exotic plants have been brought to the Isle of Man, expanding the wild flora to more than double its native quota. The first plants that came were Stone Age accidents, mixed in with imported crop seeds and unwittingly sown on the land. These cornfield annuals have been added to ever since, so plants such as cornflower which may have become extinct on the Island many times in the past have re-appeared because of reintroduction.

Orange hawkweed (or fox and cubs) is a common lawn weed originating from south and central Europe. *(Barbara Spiers)*

Red valerian – a Mediterranean plant which can grow with almost no soil and has colonised walls and waste places across the Island. *(Mike Goldie)*

Manx palms greet visitors at Ronaldsway Airport. *(Miles Cowsill - Lily Publications)*

Manx Fuchsia. *(Mike Goldie).*

Next to arrive were herbs, brought over for medicines, dyes, flavourings and other household and spiritual uses. Alexanders, sweet cicely and dame's violet (*Hesperis matronalis*) are among the plants that have 'escaped' to become wild flowers. Many others such as vervain and peppermint (*Mentha X piperata*) never really became wild and are still only found around gardens they were originally grown in.

As a seafaring nation the Manx people travelled and traded widely and brought back plants such as cultivated daffodils (probably from Holland), and many more besides.

Sycamore, from central Europe, was one of the first plants to be imported to improve the landscape. It has been here for 400 years or so and is the most common broadleaf tree. It is hardy, fast growing, resistant to exposure and its winged 'helicopter' seeds spread the tree far and wide. Sycamore is unpopular with many conservationists in the British Isles as it spreads into native woodlands, displacing other trees, but on the Isle of Man it makes a welcome addition to the landscape. Maturity comes after 100 years, when it develops a rugged bark and a broad canopy, so most of the Island's sycamores have their best years ahead of them. Sycamore supports a small variety of insects but they occur in huge quantities, making the tree more popular with foraging birds than native trees are. In fact, the only other introduced plant species which has had a bigger effect than sycamore on the Island's landscape is European gorse.

The collectors of the 19th century were responsible for introducing more plants to the Island than all those before them. Paid plant hunters searched every corner of the world for specimens to add to the collections and gardens of rival organisations and individuals, and many species found their way into Manx gardens and countryside.

Most introduced conifer trees later used in forestry would find it impossible to spread beyond the plantations given the current regimes for burning and sheep grazing. However, this does not mean that they wouldn't spread given the chance. Small open areas within plantations are rapidly colonised by Sitka spruce and lodgepole pine (*Pinus contorta*), and these two species would likewise rapidly colonise the mountains if management of the uplands was withdrawn.

Plants continue to be introduced into Island gardens and open public spaces. Many are new hybrids and cultivated varieties that could never exist outside a garden setting, but it is thought that one in ten introduced species could survive in the wild, and one in ten of these could become invasive.

Manx Fuchsia (*Fuchsia Magellanica*)

Introduced to the British Isles in 1823, and to the Isle of Man less than a decade later, this hardy fuchsia came from the barren, windy and wet southern tip of South America. It was soon established as a popular shrub across the western British Isles, where it found the humid conditions, cool summers and mild winters to its liking.

On the Isle of Man it has long been planted as decorative hedging and in shrubberies, and is so familiar it is known locally as the Manx fuchsia. Most planting dates back to the Victorian and Edwardian times, evident from the number of ruined cottages (tholtans) which have overgrown specimens surrounding them. The enthusiasm for the fuchsia is manifested at the Ballamodha Straight, a two-mile stretch of road where the sod hedges are topped with the shrub, creating a beautiful feature (the work of a Mr Winkle of Foxdale).

In their native home fuchsias are pollinated by hummingbirds flocking to the flowers, but on the Isle of Man the job is done by bees, hoverflies and moths (the flower is particularly loved by the hummingbird hawk moth) which patronise the flowers in large numbers. Occasionally, berries containing fertile seeds are formed, but the plant normally spreads as the result of people dumping garden refuse in the countryside, or of course by deliberate planting.

In warmer climates such as New Zealand and Hawaii, the plant produces much more seed and spreads rapidly into the wild. It is considered an invasive weed in these countries and costly control measures have been introduced to eradicate it.

Manx Palm (*Cordyline australis*)

This was introduced to the Isle of Man in 1823 – the same year as the Manx fuchsia – and like the fuchsia tolerates the cool summers and exposed conditions of the western British Isles. It is a New Zealand plant and has many names. The

Montbretia growing on a beach at Langness Lighthouse. A hybrid garden plant first bred in France, and still popular in gardens for its pretty orange flowers, montbretia has now colonised sod hedges, riversides and coastal sites and pushes out native flora. It is also being deliberately introduced into the countryside. *(Ian Costain)*

Japanese knotweed at Kewaigue. It has completely overgrown this stream and is rapidly colonising riverbanks all over the Island.

Maori name, ti kouka, has stuck with it, but in Britain it is more commonly called the cabbage palm or, in the West Country, the Torbay palm. By the same token, as the tree is very popular on the Island too, the Manx have adopted it as their own.

Manx palm is one of the first plants visitors see when arriving at Ronaldsway; some of the best specimens are displayed in the central reservation of the road outside the airport. In its native country this tree can become very fat and live for hundreds of years, but on the Island it is a short-lived palm and rarely exceeds 5-6 metres in height. It does, however, thrive in the most exposed conditions where few other trees could grow upright.

Despite its name, Manx palm is not a real palm and is more closely related to yuccas. It flowers and sets seed very commonly, but as the seed rarely establishes in the wild it cannot truly be called a wild flower.

Alexanders

Invasive plants

Occasionally an introduced plant is so successful that it starts to compete with the native wild flowers, slowly nudging them out of their wild habitat. These invasive exotics can overrun large areas of wild flowers and be very costly and difficult to control.

Most invasive exotics were introduced as ornamental plants in the 19th century. These include the giant hogweed (*Heracleum mantegazzianum*), montbretia (*Crocosmia x crocosmiiflora*) and Japanese Knotweed (*Fallopia japonica*). Rhododendron (*Rhododendron ponticum*), a shrub that has covered whole mountains in the British Isles, has not become a problem on the Isle of Man.

Himalayan balsam (*Impatiens glandulifera*) only escaped into the wild in the 1960s but is now colonising riverbanks across the Island. It is an annual plant which goes from seedling to head height in just a few months, pushing out established riverside vegetation, and spreading its seed further by a seed pod which explodes with some force when touched .

One of the Island's invasive plants was not introduced at all but made its way here via sea currents. Common cord grass (*Spartina anglica*) naturally hybridised and then evolved from an introduced American and a native European cord grass around Southampton in the late 19th century. It has spread around coastal saltmarshes since, arriving around the Isle of Man in the 1970s. The spread of this species on to the Island's shores is both a blessing and a curse. It grows on and smothers mud used as feeding sites for coastal birds, but it also extends saltmarsh at a much faster rate, allowing more interesting plants to colonise in its wake. Colonies of common cord grass on the Island have proved to be fairly short lived.

Japanese Knotweed

The most invasive and problematic of all wild flowers on the Isle of Man, Japanese knotweed has spread to most rivers, particularly around Douglas and the River Neb. Introduced to the British Isles in 1825 as an ornamental plant, knotweed was admired for its vigorous growth and exotic architectural structure. Its easy-to-grow characteristics led to its rapid spread by enthusiastic gardeners, but it soon escaped into the wild.

Japanese knotweed has both male and female plants, but fortunately there are unlikely to be any male plants on the Island so it cannot spread by seed. Unfortunately, it can spread by the shortest bit of stem or root deposited on bare ground, so cutting the plant back may have inadvertently helped knotweed to spread in the past. It grows to 2 metres tall and shades out almost all other plants underneath its colonies, which can become huge. While riversides are the most usual place to find it, this plant grows almost anywhere, including through tarmac, on beaches and up mountains. The Isle of Man Government, concerned by the spread of Japanese knotweed, has listed it as an 'injurious weed'. If you live on the Island and think you have the plant on your land, contact the Department of Agriculture Fisheries and Forestry for advice on how to control it.

Other newcomers

The majority of new plants which become established on the Island are from other parts of the British Isles or the near continent and happily co-exist naturally with the native wild flowers over much of their range. Most of these plants have been introduced by accident; for example, through imported grass seed or as weeds with horticultural plants.

Pink purslane.

Yellow bartsia (*Parentucellia viscosa*), a meadow flower from the West Country, was first seen on the Island in the 1950s and is now common alongside native plants on

Yellow bartsia, a relative of yellow rattle, flowers in late summer.

some of the best meadow nature reserves.

Spotted hawkweed (*Hieracium maculatum*), with its spotted leaves and yellow flowers, was first seen in the 1970s at the Braaid, where every spring a large colony still brightens up stone walls along a 50-metre stretch of road.

Pink purslane (*Claytonia sibirica*) from North America has colonised many shady riverbanks and wetlands in the last 50 years, but unlike Japanese knotweed it grows among native flora rather than smothering it.

Winter heliotrope (*Petasites fragrans*). This introduced plant is noted for its fragrant mid-winter flowers and large round leaves. *(Ian Costain)*

Eglantine rose (*Rosa rubiginosa*), or sweet briar, was introduced from elsewhere in the British Isles as a cottage garden favourite, but is now found on sand dunes in the north of the Island – as at Cronk y Bing, where the scattered shrubs provide shelter for small birds but never smother the dune vegetation below.

There are many other newcomers to the Island and more are bound to appear in the future. Manx residents reading this book are asked not to introduce more plants to the wild; such species can behave in unpredictable and ecologically damaging ways and pose a threat to native flora (and, you could also be breaking the law).

Dutch Elm Disease

Not all invaders damaging to the Island's wild flora are plants. Dutch elm disease is a fungal (*Ophiostoma novo-ulmi*) infection spread by bark beetles (*Scolytus scolytus*). The fungus kills elm (*Ulmus spp.*) trees by blocking the flow of water in the tree, leading to rapid death of branches and soon the whole tree. This disease has only been on the Island since the 1990s and despite control attempts a few trees are killed every year.

Mature elm trees are still a common sight on the Island. *(Miles Cowsill - Lily Publications)*

Dutch elm disease has wiped out most mature elm populations in England, Wales, Ireland and southern Scotland (as well as in most of continental Europe and North America), so saving Manx elm populations is particularly important. The Isle of Man government has imposed control measures to restrict the movement of cut elm and to identify elms which show symptoms (such as yellowing of leaves in crowns) and to rapidly fell and burn affected trees. Warm weather encourages the offending bark beetles to become more active, so hotter summers are likely to make it more difficult to deal with the problem. The good news is that although the disease has not yet been beaten it is under control, and Manx elms look to have a secure future on the Island.

Three cornered leek has rapidly spead along the roadsides since its introduction. *(Ian Costain)*

Preserving Manx native flowers

Perhaps the most damaging introductions are those from other parts of the British Isles of species which are native to the Island. Manx native wild flowers are specially adapted to local conditions and over the past 10,000 years have become subtly different from other populations of the same species. Growing wild flowers has become one of the popular pleasures of gardening, but in the past most wild flower stock for gardens has been imported. Unfortunately, such wild flowers will slowly dilute the native gene pool, contributing to the destruction of global biodiversity.

Wild flower
conservation

The idea that Manx wild flowers are precious and need conserving is not a new one. In 1900 there was concern that royal fern (*Osmunda regalis*), a large fern found mostly in the Ballaugh Curragh, was being dug up and taken off the Island by the cartload. Observers also noted that most of these plants died before they reached the gardens they were intended to ornament. Fortunately, it looks as if royal fern populations recovered as they are a common sight in the Ballaugh Curragh today.

Four different species of orchids, some in large colonies, grow at Ronaldsway airport.

Royal fern. *(Linda Moore)*

Despite the wide appreciation of Manx wild flowers, their active conservation on the Isle of Man was slow to get off the ground. The Manx Trust for Nature Conservation (later renamed Manx Wildlife Trust) was founded in 1973 and it acquired nature reserves soon afterwards. By 2004 the Trust was managing 21 nature reserves, in addition to operating a programme of environmental education and campaigning for conservation of the Island's natural heritage. Two visitor centres, at Scarlett and the Ayres, are run by the Trust to explain the significance of these two important sites. The Trust also has a junior branch, called Wildlife Watch, which meets regularly around the Island to look at different aspects of the natural world, including wild flowers.

Wall pepper (*Sedum acre*) in rooftops in Castletown. Subsequent renovation has destroyed this unexpected colony of wild flowers. *(Mike Goldie)*

Red Campion. *(Barbara Spiers)*

Drainage trench at the Curragh. *(Manx National Heritage)*

The Island's first piece of conservation legislation was the Curraghs Acquisition Act of 1963. This enabled the government to purchase the core areas of the Ballaugh Curragh for the nation. In 1990 Tynwald passed the Wildlife Act, making it illegal to dig up wild plants without landowners' consent and listing those plant species specifically protected from digging up, picking or destruction.

The Act also made it possible for the government to protect land with special conservation importance by designating Areas of Special Scientific Interest and National Nature Reserves as appropriate. The Department of Agriculture, Fisheries and Forestry is the body tasked with implementing the Wildlife Act along with other wildlife conservation commitments.

In 2002 the government piloted the voluntary Manx Agri-environment Scheme for farmers. While traditionally farmers have been subsidised to produce foods efficiently, this new initiative promotes good stewardship of the land by rewarding landowners for farming in an ecologically sensitive way. This means that enhancing and creating wild flower meadows, sod hedges, ponds and other precious habitats will now be an asset to farmers rather than a liability. Furthermore, under the Wildlife Act, landowners can also enter into 'management agreements', whereby they receive payment from the government to manage land for wildlife such as orchids, lapwings and corncrakes.

Interest in nature conservation on the Isle of Man goes way beyond the remit of institutional organisations. Many individuals have created private bird sanctuaries and nature reserves on pockets of land. People with modest gardens grow wild flowers and put out food and nest boxes for wild birds. Conservation and the environment are a part of the school curriculum and some schools have set aside wildlife areas as a teaching aid.

Ballaugh Curragh

This 1,000 acre (405 ha) area in the north-west is the largest wetland in the Island. Thousands of years ago it was a lake – Lake Andreas – but over a long period it became silted up with gravel

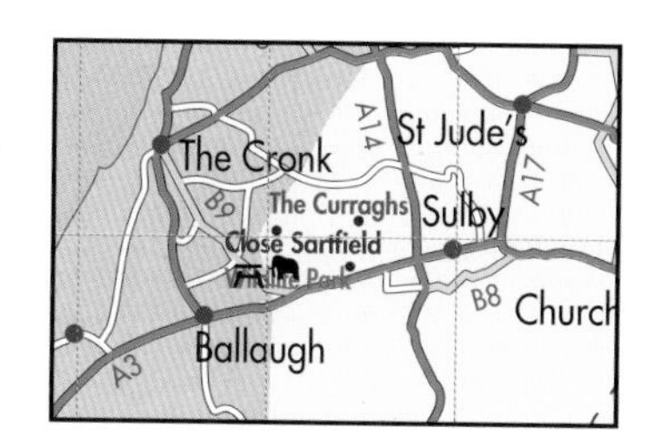

Marsh St John's wort. *(Manx National Heritage)*

and sand sediments from the mountains. Choked with vegetation, the stagnant waterlogged conditions prevented the plants from decaying properly, and peat began to form. The resulting Curragh was too wet for cultivation and would have been much as the willow curragh and bog vegetation are today.

Around the 1500s, efforts were made to drain the wetlands around the edges and reclaim the land for agriculture. Draining was difficult – the site was flat and just 10 metres above sea level – but eventually this 'intack' land was suitable for pasture, meadows and cultivated crops. Digging up large amounts of deep peat for fuel continued well into the 20th century, recreating areas of open water which form the few remaining ponds in the Curragh today.

In 1963, to help preserve the wild bird populations, the Curragh Acquisition

Slate gate posts, now overgrown with ivy, are clues to the history of the area. *(Manx National Heritage)*

Act brought the wildest central areas, already overgrown with willow, into Isle of Man Government ownership. In addition to this conservation measure, the Curraghs Wildlife Park was created. In 1978 the area outside the wildlife park came under the control of Manx National Heritage, which continues to manage it for nature conservation.

You can visit the Curragh today via the road which marks the northern boundary of Manx National Heritage land and the small paths which cross this very wild site. There's a tangle of lichen and ivy (*Hedera helix*), encrusted willow and areas of bog and open water. But the remains of agriculture can still be seen too in the shape of overgrown sod hedges and slate gate posts and old roads. The sod hedges are particularly noted for the royal fern and holly growing on them in abundance. The bog areas contain the Island's largest concentrations of bog myrtle, a low-growing shrub with spicy scented leaves that are a potent midge repellent. A recent plant discovery for the Island – the common wintergreen (*Pyrola minor*) – was made in the Curragh nearby the Wildlife Park.

The outer areas away from government ownership are a mixture of curragh, meadow, unimproved pasture and intensively farmed fields. Sadly, in parts of this area, there has been a recent trend towards agricultural improvement at the cost of nature conservation, but Manx Wildlife Trust and most landowners try to maintain the balance of meadow and willow curragh.

As well as the meadow and curragh wild flowers, the area is noted for interesting fauna such as red-necked wallabies (*Macropus rufogriseus*) – escapees from the wildlife park which have formed a small but elusive wild colony in the curragh.

The Wildflowers of Mann Project

Launched in 2000 with joint funding from several government departments (Agriculture Fisheries and Forestry, Tourism and Leisure, Transport) and Manx National Heritage, this originated as an idea to colour up the Manx countryside and developed into a major project to promote and conserve Manx wild flowers.

A project manager was appointed to work under the guidance of a

The Wild Flowers of Mann project worked with the Department of Transport to create a wild flower verge at Kewaigue bridge. These cornfield annuals are flowering to spectacular effect in the first year. *(Ian Costain)*

The project's wild garden at St John's shows how to grow wild flowers alongside garden plants such as sunflowers.

committee drawn from the four funding bodies, members of Tynwald and organisations such as Manx Farmers Union and Isle of Man Friends of the Earth. The first task was to make available native wild flowers for use in new projects. Seed was collected from nature reserves and from wild places where plants were most likely to be of pure Manx origin. The seeds were then sown and grown on before being planted out as seed crops. This time-consuming process has resulted in a field which produces an annual crop of 20 different types of wild flower seed to sow in new conservation projects. The seed is also sold in packets for anyone who wishes to buy into wild flowers and grow them at home.

As well as supplying wild flower seed and plants, the project is also an advice service. This is accessible through a variety of means – visits to schools, farms and gardens and advisory leaflets and guides. At St John's Mill, the project has created

The one-acre field at Knockaloe where the Wildflowers of Mann Project grows native seed has become a summer magnet to bees and butterflies.

Heath spotted orchid.

and runs the Wild Flower Garden to show how wild flowers not only fit comfortably into a garden but can also enhance a natural space to make it look original and interesting.

Although planting lots of native wild flowers is important, the project is aimed at promoting greater understanding, knowledge and interest in the Island's outstanding natural flora – and talks, guided walks and working with school children and community groups are all helping to achieve this.

Orchids

No other wild flowers have a name with quite the same resonance as orchids. They conjure up an image of exotic and elusive species, with bold, fanciful flowers. Many species of orchid such as common twayblade (*Listera ovata*) and butterfly orchid (*Platanthera spp.*) are fairly unremarkable at first sight (though fascinating on closer inspection), their pale green or white flowers blending in with grass remarkably well.

Heath spotted orchids (*Dactylorhiza maculata*) occur in a colony of 100,000 in Close Sartfield Nature Reserve, and a few can be found in many wet pastures and meadows. It is still a thrill to see orchids in the wild and some, such as northern marsh orchid (*Dactylorhiza purpurella*), pyramidal orchid (*Anacamptis pyramidalis*) and bee orchid (*Ophrys apifera*) look quite exotic.

While many plants have developed relationships with fungi, orchids have taken the relationship to extremes. Orchids can spread themselves hundreds of miles by virtue of their masses of dust-like seed. The payback is that the seed cannot germinate by itself as it comes with no food store – a problem ingeniously solved by allowing itself to become infected with fungus. Instead of the fungus feeding on the seed, the opposite occurs. For the first year or more of an orchid's life it is leafless, feeding off the fungus until it is strong enough to produce foliage. From this moment the role of the fungus is not so critical, but the plant still grows better with the infection. It is likely that as the orchid matures it starts to feed the fungus as much as the other way round, but this can take many years. Some orchids such as bee orchids flower so well in their first flowering year that they exhaust their energy reserves and die, though like most

Twayblade. *(Edgar Boyes)*

orchids their lives can span decades.

The tiny seeds enable orchids to pop up in unexpected and remote places. Dense flowered orchids *(Neotinea maculata)* normally only grow around the Mediterranean and Ireland but appeared at the Ayres in the 1960s. After establishing a flourishing colony for a few years they declined and it now seems likely they are gone from the Island.

All orchid species are protected under the Wildlife Act.

Conservation on roadside verges

On a day-to-day basis most peoples' encounters with wild flowers are those they see from the inside of a car, van or bus. If it were not for roadside verges, many of us would not be familiar with plants such as harebells, primroses and fairy flowers.

The majority of verges and hedges on the Island are still rich in the more common wild flowers and have become a refuge for many plants pushed out of farmland. Verges provide many of the Island's habitats, such as curragh and heath,

Roadsides like this one in Jurby East remain rich in wild flowers due to sensible management.
(Miles Cowsill - Lily Publications)

Wood sedge (*Carex sylvatica*) grows in Summerhill Glen and just a few other woodland sites on the Island. *(Miles Cowsill - Lily Publications)*

Spring sandwort (*Minuartia verna*) occurs only on mine 'deads' on Bradda Head.

A pair of sea stacks at Port Grenagh are the only Manx home for silver-leaved sea wormwood (*Seriphidium maritimum*). *(Miles Cowsill - Lily Publications)*

Parsley fern (*Cryptogamma crispa*) is found only in South Barrule quarry.
(Miles Cowsill - Lily Publications)

but as the mowing of most verges is similar to that in traditional meadows, the plants found in each are similar too and include meadow buttercup, meadowsweet and knapweed (*Centaurea nigra*).

Maintaining verges for wild flowers is the task of the Department of Transport (DoT) and is a difficult one. Cutting early removes the flowers before they have chance to seed, cutting late can make narrow roads dangerous. If verges were not cut at all, the more delicate wild flowers would be smothered by gorse, bramble (*Rubus fruticosus* agg.), bracken and coarse grasses.

In 1991 the DoT set up the HEDGE (Highways Edge Discussion Group on Ecology) committee of road managers, ecologists and interested parties, in an endeavour to formulate the best management practices for roadside vegetation. Part of the remit is to help designate the best verges as 'conservation' or 'sensitive' verges. These are verges that will act as linear nature reserves and be carefully managed to maintain their conservation interest.

Manx Wildlife Trust (a HEDGE participant) surveyed the Island's verges from 1991-1996 and found many of them to be very rich in wild flower species. On average each contained over 70 species, but one boasted nearly 170. From this survey 12 conservation and 14 sensitive verges were designated.

Climate change

One of the biggest threats to wild flowers is the spectre of global climate change. It is most likely that the Isle of Man's unpredictable weather will become even less predictable and that overall the climate will be warmer – though some forecasts suggest it could be much colder!

What this will mean for Manx wild flowers is also hard to predict accurately. It is probable that some species reliant on cold mountain conditions will become extinct. Others will be unable to tolerate the drier conditions. Bluebells could be restricted to damp woodlands. Wetlands could become drier, with subsequent loss of species dependent on them. The Curragh could be dominated by birch and ash trees, bog plants retreating to the wettest areas.

On the positive side there are likely to be winners too. Many Island plants now considered rare could become more common, such as some species of

Flowering pasture. *(Mike Goldie)*

Knapweed.

Thrift. *(Vicki Harrop)*

Autumn hawkbit – one of many plants with dandelion-like flowers which add colour to flowering meadows and lawns.

orchid. Certain exotic plants, previously restricted to gardens, may be able to grow in the wild. Hottentot-fig (*Carpobrotus edulis*), which swamps coastal vegetation in Cornwall and the Channel Islands, could seriously damage Manx coastal flora in the event of climate change..

Conservationists on the Island can help minimise the impact of global warming. In some wetlands the water table can be manipulated to stay high in times of drought. Other problems which threaten to put a strain on wild flora populations, such as pollution and the fragmentation of wild flower habitats, can also be tackled.

Ultimately the only real solution to this potentially massive problem is a worldwide commitment to mitigating as far as possible the causes of global climate change. This would ensure the survival of native Manx wild flowers – but the fear is that many species will have become extinct before this will happen.

Manx wild flower gardening

Growing Manx wild flowers not only helps their conservation – it brings with it other wildlife and a more natural, romantic feel to a garden. Wild flowers fit easily into a normal garden but a better way of using them is to mimic their natural habitats, such as shingle cove, flowering meadow or Manx heath. Wild flower gardening is not about having a neglected garden of thistles and brambles; this is good for some wildlife but does not make for an attractive place for people.

Spring bluebell meadow.

Wild flowers are not always the easy option either, as creating natural areas can take a lot of preparation, though the results will reward your effort. Wild flower gardens also tend not to be 'instant' in the way we have come to expect of modern gardens, but every year they mature, change and improve in a way which is very satisfying.

Manx wild flowers are available to buy as plants and seeds and are easy to grow. Just one packet of seeds can be turned into 200 or more plants to create the beginnings of a garden meadow featuring a favourite flower such as harebell or ragged robin – and by the very next year your meadow could be a swathe of flowers and colour.

The wild flower border

Wild flowers can be grown in garden borders separated from but alongside other garden plants. Traditional cottage garden plants such as lupins, delphiniums and honesty will fit well with the informal look of wild flowers. For best effect the border should be in a sheltered sunny spot to help attract insects.

Pack your flower border full of plants. Woodland wild flowers can grow among the taller plants at the middle and back of the garden, with the shorter plants typical of, say, coastal areas at the front. You don't need to over-design your garden border; remember, a jumbled random effect is desired, and the plants will sow themselves wherever they please in future years. Planting in groups of three, five or more is recommended so that each type of plant is not lost in a messy blur.

In the first year or two there will be lots of gaps while plants become established. These can be filled with cornfield annuals such as poppies, sown by scattering a pinch of seeds into any gap. Some wild flowers such as ox-eye daisies seed themselves around a garden a little too enthusiastically, so laying down a wood chip or bark mulch is best to stop them becoming too rampant.

Don't tidy up your border at the end of the season as many insects will overwinter in the dead stems, or at the base of plants. Most of these insects will be predators such as beetles, ladybirds, hoverflies and lacewings, and they will help control pests the following year.

PLANTS FOR THE WILD FLOWER BORDER

Best for the back

Bulbous buttercup
Common knapweed
Common valerian
Devil's-bit scabious
Fairy flower
Field scabious
Foxglove
Hemp agrimony
Lady's smock
Meadow buttercup
Mullein
Ox-eye daisy
Purple loosestrife
Ragged robin
Sneezewort
Sweet cicely
Teasel
Tufted vetch
White campion
Wild carrot

Around their ankles

Bluebells
Bugle
Dog violet
Ferns
Germander speedwell
Greater bird's-foot trefoil
Lady's bedstraw
Pignut
Primrose
Selfheal
Tormentil
Wood anenome

At the front

Bell heather
Bird's-foot trefoil
Goldenrod
Harebell
Kidney vetch
Mouse-ear hawkweed
Sea campion
Sheepsbit
Spring squill
Sweet violet
Thrift
Wild thyme

Cornfield annuals. *(Ian Costain)*

Cornfield annuals

A cornfield annual patch is one of the simplest and most colourful wild flower displays. Its advantages are that it is quick and easy to create and the rapid results make it an ideal children's project.

Cultivate soil in a sunny spot so that it is weed free with a fine tilth, scatter the seed in winter or spring at about 2-4 grams per square metre, and rake it in. An early sowing in autumn or winter will flower in late spring and early summer and a late sowing (up to June) will flower in mid to late summer, through to autumn.

Weed out docks, thistles and other unwanted plants as soon as they show and then leave the site to flower. In late autumn, once the seeds have fallen for

THE BEST SPECIES ARE...

Poppy *Long-headed poppy* *Cornflower*
Corn marigold *Corncockle*

BUT YOU CAN ALSO ADD...

Corn chamomile *Wild pansy* *Fumitory*
Scarlet pimpernel *Flax*
White campion *Corn spurry*

Nature has a habit of showing us perfect plant combinations, such as here with ragged robin, meadow buttercup and crested dog's-tail on a wet verge near St Mark's.

the birds, clear out any weeds and rake the site over. The site will re-seed itself every year.

Experiment with the plot by adding barley or other cereals for the authentic cornfield look, or add your favourite annuals such as snapdragons or sunflowers for a more exotic look.

Perfect garden meadows

A meadow can be as large or as small as you want and will show off wild flowers in their most natural setting. Meadows do not work well on very fertile soil as the lush grass it grows just swamps out most wild flowers. It can take years for a meadow to become properly established and you may have to tinker with how you manage it to best suit your site – but it is the most satisfying garden feature when you succeed.

AN A-Z OF MEADOW AND LAWN FLOWERS

Flowers for a spring meadow

Bird's-foot trefoil ■ ■ ■ ■ ■
Bugle ■ ■ ■
Bulbous buttercup ■ ■ ■ ■ ■
Cat's-ear ■ ■ ■ ■ ■
Common sorrel ■ ■ ■ ■
Common valerian ■ ■ ■
Daisy ■ ■ ■ ■ ■ ■
Fairy flower ■ ■ ■
Germander speedwell ■ ■ ■ ■
Kidney vetch ■ ■ ■
Lady's smock ■ ■ ■ ■
Lesser celandine ■ ■ ■ ■
Meadow buttercup ■ ■ ■ ■
Meadowsweet ■ ■ ■ ■
Mouse-ear hawkweed ■ ■ ■ ■
Ox-eye daisy ■ ■ ■ ■ ■
Pignut ■ ■ ■ ■ ■
Primrose ■ ■ ■ ■
Ragged robin ■ ■ ■
Red clover ■ ■ ■ ■
Yellow Rattle ■ ■ ■ ■ ■ ■

Flowers for a summer meadow

Autumn hawkbit ■ ■ ■ ■ ■
Bird's-foot trefoil ■ ■ ■ ■ ■
Cat's-ear ■ ■ ■ ■ ■
Common knapweed ■ ■ ■ ■
Common sorrel ■ ■ ■ ■
Common valerian ■ ■ ■
Daisy ■ ■ ■ ■ ■ ■
Devil's-bit scabious ■ ■ ■ ■
Fairy flower ■ ■ ■
Field scabious ■ ■ ■ ■
Greater bird's-foot trefoil ■ ■
Harebell ■ ■ ■ ■ ■
Lady's bedstraw ■ ■ ■ ■
Marsh woundwort ■ ■ ■
Meadow buttercup ■ ■ ■ ■
Meadowsweet ■ ■ ■ ■
Meadow vetchling ■ ■ ■
Ox-eye daisy ■ ■ ■ ■ ■
Ragged robin ■ ■ ■
Red clover ■ ■ ■ ■
Selfheal ■ ■ ■ ■ ■
Sneezwort ■ ■ ■ ■
Yarrow ■ ■ ■ ■

Flowers to add to a lawn

Autumn hawkbit ■ ■ ■ ■ ■
Bird's-foot trefoil ■ ■ ■ ■ ■
Bugle ■ ■ ■
Bulbous buttercup ■ ■ ■ ■ ■
Cat's-ear ■ ■ ■ ■ ■
Daisy ■ ■ ■ ■ ■ ■
Germander speedwell ■ ■ ■ ■
Harebell ■ ■ ■ ■ ■
Kidney vetch ■ ■ ■
Lesser celandine ■ ■ ■ ■
Mouse-ear hawkweed ■ ■ ■ ■
Ox-eye daisy ■ ■ ■ ■ ■
Primrose ■ ■ ■ ■
Selfheal ■ ■ ■ ■ ■
Wild thyme ■ ■ ■ ■

■ **Wet**
■ **Well Drained**
■ **Dry**
■ **Acid**
■ **Neutral**
■ **Alkaline**

Mowing a meadow is essential for several reasons: to keep down the fertility of the soil, to prevent coarse grasses dominating, and to stop a thatch of dead grass from developing. Always remove grass and hay cuttings from your meadow. To enjoy your meadow fully, mow a path through the middle so you do not have to trample flowers to see it properly.

Garden meadows are best started from scratch, by cultivating a piece of ground and raking it flat. A meadow seed mix will contain 4/5 grass and 1/5 wild flower seed and should be sown at 4 grams per square metre. The seed can be sown at any time but if sown in late spring or summer it will have to be watered to germinate. Soon after seeds begin to germinate, try picking out thistle, dock and nettle seedlings as these will cause problems in your meadow later on.

There are essentially two types of meadow you can grow: the spring meadow, which flowers in spring and is cut in July and then throughout summer; and the summer meadow, which is mown in spring (until about May) and flowers in summer.

The types of plant you can grow will be different in each. A spring meadow can be grown in semi-shade and is a good place to put naturalised spring bulbs such as bluebells and snowdrops. Throughout summer you can treat your spring meadow like a lawn. A summer meadow is best for butterflies and because it flowers in summer is often the preferred type for a garden.

At the same time that you sow the seed, it is best to put in plants such as scabious, lady's smock, bugle and harebell as small 'plug' plants to help the seed establish. In more mature grassland it may be better to plant larger plants to do this, as smaller ones could become swamped.

In the first year, as few plants will flower, it does no harm to mow your meadow more often to keep it tidy and stop it looking a little drab. Alternatively, cornfield annuals can be mixed in with the seed to give some colour while the other plants get established. Make sure to sow no more than 1 gram per square metre or the annuals will swamp out the meadow flowers and grass.

Grass parasites such as yellow rattle will help keep the grass from dominating the wild flowers. Sow this in your meadow every autumn until it

A-Z OF PLANTS FOR WATERLOGGED OR SHALLOW WATER SITES

Bog bean
Branched bur reed
Greater spearwort
Marsh cinquefoil
Marsh marigold
Purple loosestrife
Water forget-me-not
Water mint
Yellow flag

A-Z OF PLANTS FOR WET OR DAMP SITES

Angelica
Bugle
Common valerian
Devil's-bit scabious
Greater bird's-foot trefoil
Hemp agrimony
Lady fern
Lady's smock
Lesser spearwort
Meadow buttercup
Meadowsweet
Opposite-leaved golden saxifrage
Ragged robin
Royal fern
Sneezewort
Wild garlic

Yellow flag iris, one of the most familiar pondside plants, still grows in abundance in the wild in parts of the Island. *(Ian Costain)*

becomes established.

Most established lawns have many wild flowers such as daisies and dandelions in them. Leave them to flower for a month in mid-summer when the grass is hardly growing so that you enjoy a virtual meadow effect without ever losing a usable lawn. You can add more flowers as small plants in autumn to make a lawn more flowery still.

Ponds and wetlands

Ponds are often described as magnets for wildlife, and with good reason. Within days of creating a pond you will attract visitors such as dragonflies and sparrows. Within a year your pond will look as though it's been there for ages.

Here are a few important pointers to creating your wildlife-friendly pond:

- Include shallow areas for wildlife access and because they are warmer.
- Fringe the pond with wetland vegetation to attract shy animals.
- Do not introduce fish as they gobble up all the pond life.
- Never introduce any material from your pond into the wild.
- Try to make your pond at least 5 metres across to allow marginal plants to encroach without choking the whole pond.

There are many manuals on how to create a pond and the materials you can use. Clay-lined ponds are the best for wildlife but you should really take professional advice – clay is much trickier to lay than other liners.

Create wetlands around your pond or in naturally wet parts of the garden. By planting into bare wet ground in spring, a thick wetland vegetation will be well established by summer. Weed out grasses unless you want a wet meadow effect, and tidy up in late winter, when you can also remove unwanted plants. Wetlands soon grow into a jumble of colour and form, so do not be too fussy about 'design' or your planting plan.

Coastal sites and sod hedges

Coastal plants grow in much the same conditions as a rock garden, with poor sharply-drained soils and full sun. They can survive the most exposed sites, but tend to be uncompetitive if used alongside other plants in a rich garden soil. Sod hedges share many plants in common with coastal sites as they have the same requirements for sharp drainage and sun. Coastal planting can be in many forms. Maritime grassland can be established and managed similarly to other meadows but will only need mowing once a year. Coastal grasslands are dominated by red fescue grass – the best grass to grow with your coastal plants.

Alternatively, coastal plants can be grown in a scree bed, with a fine gravel mulch and protruding rocks, much as found on a rocky Manx coast. These beds will require little maintenance as long as the soil is very poor and free-draining.

Shingle gardens that mimic pebble beaches need a 50cm-deep layer of shingle and coarse sand with a shingle topping. In this type of garden, plants are

AN A-Z OF COASTAL AND SOD HEDGE PLANTS

Autumn hawkbit
Bell heather
Bird's-foot trefoil
Burnet rose
Cat's-ear
Foxglove
Goldenrod
Harebell
Heath bedstraw
Kidney vetch
Lady's bedstraw
Mouse-ear hawkweed
Sea campion (coastal only)
Sheepsbit
Spring squill (coastal only)
Thrift (coastal only)
Tormentil

For a shingle garden

Burnet rose
Long-headed poppy
Sea bindweed
Sea holly
Sea mayweed
Sea rocket

Peel Castle. *(Vicki Harrop)*

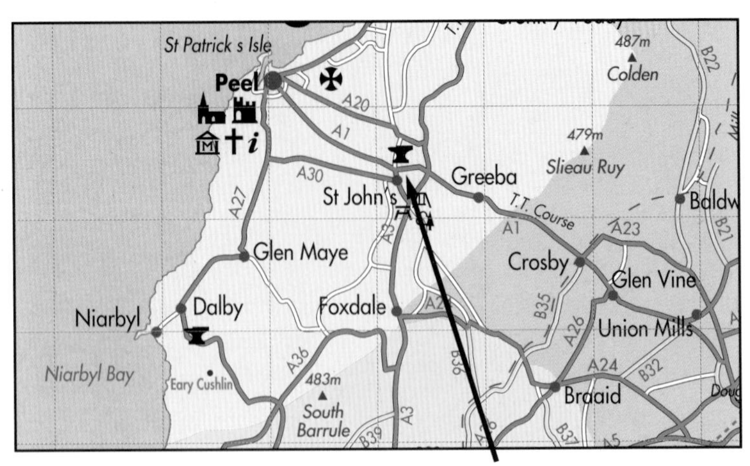

The Wildflower Garden can be found at Tynwald Mills Shopping Centre, just past the main shopping area next to St John's Mill.

widely spaced to give each enough space to grow to full size. The garden can be ornamented with shells and driftwood and dried seaweed for a more authentic effect. Exotic plants such as cardoon, fennel and opium poppy will grow well among the shingle wild flowers without looking out of place.

Sod hedges can be managed much like a vertical version of a normal meadow, but if you inherit an overgrown hedge you may have to spend the first two years strimming it on a rather regular basis to get rid of the rank vegetation. Apart from real seaside plants such as thrift and sea campion, most sod hedge plants will be the same as those for coastal areas for the top third of the hedge,

AN A-Z OF PLANTS FOR HEATHLAND

	Associated plants
Bell heather	*Harebell*
Bilberry	*Heath bedstraw*
Burnet rose	*Lousewort*
Ling	*Tormentil*
Western gorse	

The opening of the garden. From left to right: Bob Jeavans, William Cain, Martin Quayle MHK, Andree Dubbeldam and Jane Prescott. *(Miles Cowsill - Lily Publications)*

The Wildflower Garden in April 2004. *(Miles Cowsill - Lily Publications)*

and the same as meadow flowers for the lower two-thirds. At the base of the sod hedge also include woodland plants such as wood anemone, bluebell and primrose. If the sod hedge comes with a ditch then wetland plants such as meadowsweet and flag iris can be used. The top of a sod hedge is also a good place to get a Manx heath established.

Manx heath

Heathlands are low carpets of shrubby, acid-loving plants. If you have a sunny, well-drained, neutral-to-acid site you can create a heathland. The majority of heathland is made up of bell heather, ling and western gorse, which gradually take over and every 5-10 years need cutting right back to allow the other plants a chance to grow. Apart from this, heathland needs almost no maintenance.

Start creating your heathland by cultivating a bare area of soil – the poorer and drier it is, the better. If you have a rich garden soil, incorporate lots of grit to aid drainage and to reduce fertility. Large rocks are a common heathland feature, so place these before planting. Plant about 10 shrubby heathland plants and 5 associated wild flowers per square metre. Bell heather (*Erica cinerea*) is prettier than the more common ling (*Calluna vulgaris*) so in a garden you may wish to plant more of these. Mulch the ground with something like shingle, grit or peat-free compost to prevent weeds from getting established.

The showcase Wild Flower Garden at St John's

Built throughout 2003, the garden's purpose is to provide a source of inspiration and information on gardening with wild flowers. It lies in the grounds of the old mill tenter field opposite Tynwald Mills. The field is so called because it was where woven cloth from the mills was placed over 2-metre-tall wooden tenter frames to dry and stretch it. It was hoped that these racks could be saved as they were still standing when the garden was being built, but sadly the wood was too rotten.

When building of the garden commenced it was overgrown with gorse, bracken and rhododendrons, but the abundance of wild flowers at the fringes – bluebells and other spring flowers – were saved and incorporated into the scheme.

Fuchsia. ***(Vicki Harrop)***

The St john's Mill Wildflower Garden. *(Cheryl Cousins)*

Butterfly Border
Mill Race
Tenter Frames
Woodland Edge

rnfield Annuals
Summer Meadow
Wildlife Ponds
Daisy lawn
Spring Meadow

Also surviving are the repaired mill races, running down the sides of the garden. These carry water which feeds the new garden pond and flows through the mill building itself.

Most features of a wild flower garden have been incorporated, including a daisy lawn, two meadows and a butterfly border which has wild flowers, cottage garden plants, herbs, bulbs and shrubs that will keep the garden flowering for most of the year. Bordering the pond are native wetland plants, and the whole garden is fringed by woodland to create a sheltered environment.

If you want to learn about wild flower gardening, this show garden at St John's is the place to come. All the help and advice you need is here – from regular workshops to information materials – and of course regular return visits over the course of the year will show you all the aspects of the site and how the garden is developing.

A27
Glen Maye
Dalby
Peel A27

FURTHER READING

Manx natural history

The starting point to learning more about the Manx countryside is Larch Garrad's **The Naturalist in the Isle of Man** (published by David & Charles, 1972). It is now out of print but Manx libraries should have a copy.

Flora of the Isle of Man by David Allen (Manx Museum, 1984) provides a list of all Island plants found in the wild and describes their distribution and status.

The eagerly-awaited **A New History of the Isle of Man: Volume I** covers much of the material contained in this book but is more academic, and is recommended for readers who wish to know more about the Manx countryside. It is expected to be published during 2004.

Plant identification

Many published books are available describing flora of the British Isles, and most are adequate for identifying wild flowers of the Isle of Man. However, specially recommended are **Wild Flower Key** by Frances Rose (Warne, 1981) and **Wild Flowers of Britain and Ireland** by Blamey, Fitter and Fitter (A & C Black, 2003).

Grasses and non-flowering plants are difficult to identify even with field guides. The best way to learn is to go on one of the short courses held regularly at various places throughout the British Isles. A widely available and useful guide is **Grasses, Sedges, Rushes and Ferns of Great Britain and Northern Europe** by Fitter, Fitter and Farrer (Collins, 1984).

Other books

Flora Britannica by Richard Mabey (Sinclair-Stevenson, 1996) is a fascinating and informative encyclopaedia of flower folklore of Great Britain and the Isle of Man.

There are many books on wild flowers and wildlife gardening, with more appearing every year – a reflection of the growing interest in these subjects. Chris Baines's **How to Make a Wildlife Garden** (Frances Lincoln Ltd, 2000), first published in 1984, is still the definitive guide on the subject.

MORE MANX NAMES FOR WILD FLOWERS

Sycamore	Shykey
Yarrow	Airh hallooin
Wild garlic	Craue
Sweet vernal grass	Faiyr sonnys
Daisy	Neaynin bane
Birch	Beih
Buddleia	Lus y toar villish
Marsh marigold	Blughtyn (p) Booalught (sing)
Lady's smock	Lus ny boaldyn
Sedge	Shiest
Cornflower	Sumark gorrym
Greater celandine	Lus ny gollan geayee
Corn marigold	Blaashag buigh
Spear thistle	Onnane shleiy
Common scurvy grass	Guilley bing
Pignut	Curlan
Sea kale	Kaayle hraie
Crested dogstail	Connane
Cocksfoot	Faiyr vollagh
Wild carrot	Carradje marrey
Foxglove	Clagggan clieau
Bluebell	Gleih vuc
Sea holly	Cullyn
Lady's bedstraw	Lus ny binshey mooar

Ground ivy	Ayr lossery
Sheepsbit	Bossan gorrym
Duckweed	Gleiy fannag
Ox-eye daisy	Bastag vane
Ragged robin	Lud ny cooag
Purple loosestrife	Lus skeaylley
Hemlock water dropwort	Emloge ushtey
Poppy	Lus y chadlee
Tormentil	Crammylt ny muc
Primrose	Sumark
Meadow buttercup	Spaag feeagh
Lesser celandine	Lus ny pileyn
Yellow rattle	Clabberey buigh
Dog rose	drughaig
Bramble	Dress
Dock	Cabbag
Pussy willow	Shellagh vooar
Broom	Jutlagh
Common chickweed	Flee
Devil's-bit scabious	Bit y jouyll
Dandelion	Lus y vinniagh
Red clover	Shamrag ny gabbil
Nettle	Onn